The Slave Who Freed Haiti

THE STORY OF TOUSSAINT LOUVERTURE

THE SLAVE WHO

FREED HAITI

The Story of Toussaint Louverture

BY **KATHARINE** SCHERMAN

Illustrated by **ADOLF DEHN**

RANDOM HOUSE · NEW YORK

Contents

Author's Note

About the name Louverture:

Toussaint was christened François Dominique Toussaint. According to Haitian custom he was given the surname Bréda, after the plantation on which he was born. Shortly after the uprising of the slaves, he adopted the surname Louverture, which is similar to the French word *l'ouverture*, meaning *the opening*. The reason for this is unknown. Some say it comes from an exclamation of a French general: "This man makes an opening wherever he goes!" Others think that it was given him by the slaves of Haiti because he opened the gates of freedom for them.

The spelling, *Louverture*, is Toussaint's own. On one or two early documents the spelling *l'Ouverture* appears. But his recognized signature was *Louverture*, and so he was addressed by all who wrote to him. It appears in this form in his memoirs and in almost all of his proclamations. All existing letters written by Toussaint are signed with this form, including two which can be found in the New York Public Library: one to Edward Stevens, American Consul-General in Haiti, and another to the French general, Laveaux.

Despite this evidence from Toussaint's own memoirs and letters, the spelling *L'Ouverture* is used in a number of encyclopedias and biographical dictionaries today. In *The Slave Who Freed Haiti* the name is spelled as Toussaint and his contemporaries spelled it—*Louverture.*

—*Katharine Scherman*

The Slave Who Freed Haiti

THE STORY OF TOUSSAINT LOUVERTURE

1

The Happy Slave

IN 1744 THE TINY, MOUNTAINOUS ISLAND OF HAITI, IN the West Indies, harbored several hundred thousand African slaves. Most of these slaves existed in a state of complete misery and degradation. They were beaten, starved, tortured and brutally overworked for the profit and amusement of their white masters. France owned Haiti then, and the little colony was one of the richest in the world. The white planters of Haiti, used to being waited on hand and foot by black slaves, had reached a height of cruelty, decadence and corruption seldom equaled. The little island was seething with unrest.

Life on Bréda plantation was somewhat different, however. It was one of the few plantations with a kind and intelligent master. On the fertile northern plain of Haiti, Bréda grew and refined sugar with the help of over a thousand slaves. The whip was used sparingly.

The field slaves, although they worked long hours, were given time to till their own land and many holidays for dancing and visiting. To the horror of his neighbors, the manager even let his smarter slaves learn to read and write and borrow books. Once in a while a faithful old slave was freed. But he still continued to live under his master's protection, tilling his own soil and employing a few slaves given to him by his master.

About 1744 on Bréda plantation, a beautiful Haitian slave girl named Pauline was married to Gaou-Guinon, the son of an African chieftain. To celebrate their wedding the master of the plantation gave a great feast. Slaves came from neighboring plantations, and there were dancing and merrymaking all night long.

The son of Pauline and Gaou-Guinon was born November 1st, All Saints Day, about 1745. He was named François Dominique Toussaint. No one knows the exact year of his birth because masters seldom kept careful records of the names and birthdays of their slaves. Slave babies often died before they were named. And even if they lived, slaves were hardly considered people.

But slavery weighed lightly on little Toussaint because he grew up on lovely Bréda plantation. Around the plantation buildings wide, flat fields of sugar cane rippled in a light breeze like a pale green lake. Along the edges of the canefields were double rows of low banana trees. The road through the fields to the dwelling house was lined with tall, graceful coconut palms, and the house itself was surrounded by them. They kept up a continuous, paper-like rustling. Here and there were groves of orange trees with bright fruit and dark green leaves. Above the plantation fields the gentler slopes of the foothills were covered with thousands of small, neat coffee trees. Still farther up were majestic mountain peaks dark with pine and mahogany.

The dwelling house of the master was a long, low structure of wood covered with whitewashed plaster. Its entrance was through a gallery of beautiful wrought-iron grill work. Immediately inside was a big, low-ceilinged room furnished sparsely, but in the current French style, with gold leaf and brocade on the chairs, tapestry on the walls. All the rooms of the house opened on this great hall. They had many windows, covered with lattices, so that the inside of the house was cool and dark.

White-robed slaves moved noiselessly around the house in bare feet, each one performing his own small particular duty. One prepared the baths; another saw to the linen; another took care of the master's wine cellar. At meals a slave stood behind each chair. The faces of these slaves were generally impassive, but when one looked at them they smiled and sprang forward. They didn't seem to have anything to do, but they gave the house an impression of exotic wealth, like a Sultan's palace.

Gaou-Guinon, Toussaint's father, was a leader among the Bréda slaves, and his little son was spared the degrading and humiliating experiences of most slaves. Since Gaou-Guinon was a native African, Toussaint was brought up as an African child, wise in the ways of his father's country. Gaou-Guinon was an aristocrat of the Arada tribe of West Africa. They were proud and intelligent people, good fighters and good farmers. He taught Toussaint the skills of the soil and the art of healing with natural herbs. He told him stories of how the Africans fought in their native country, attacking their enemies from hidden places in the woods, and then vanishing like wild animals into the shadows of the forest before they could be caught. Toussaint also learned from his father to speak the beautiful and expressive Arada language.

Little Toussaint learned quickly, but he was a sickly

The Africans attacked their enemies from hidden places

and downcast child. His mother used to murmur sadly that her little boy would not live long. When he played with the other boys, they made fun of him and called him "Little Stick" because he was so dreadfully thin. He hardly ever smiled and always kept to himself. But he had a fierce pride, and he determined to overcome his weakness. To do this he spent hours by himself climbing the steep mountains near the plantation, riding and taming the wildest horses. By the time he was fifteen, he could ride longer, swim faster and hunt better than any of the other plantation boys. They gave him a new nickname, "Centaur of the Savanna," because when he rode he seemed to be one with his horse. Even when Toussaint was very little he had a way with dumb animals. His particular love was horses, an enduring passion all of his life.

On the plantation lived a freed slave named Pierre Baptiste, a good, devout old man who took an interest in the proud, silent African child. He determined that the boy should learn more than just native African ways. First he taught Toussaint to speak French. Most of the slaves never learned the language of their masters, but used a mixture of African dialects and a French jargon called Creole. Then he taught the boy to read and write, which not one in a thousand slaves could do. Toussaint also learned from him some elementary geometry.

Though outwardly Christians, the great mass of slaves still secretly practised their ancient African rites. Unlike them Pierre Baptiste was a devout Christian. He taught his pupil the Christian principles of love and humility. And the teachings of Christ touched a sympathetic chord in the heart of the African slave boy. Brought up among humble people, gentle and kind even as a child, Toussaint developed early a profound sympathy for the oppressed and lowly. Christianity was to him the natural expression of this all-embracing sympathy. On another level the incensed display of the Catholic service appealed to him, and all his life he was to delight in its dramatic ritual. Old Pierre Baptiste had picked up a few phrases of medieval Church Latin. These almost meaningless syllables delighted the small boy. He learned them quickly, and for the rest of his life took innocent pleasure in rolling the sonorous words off his tongue and watching the awed amazement of his listeners.

Toussaint's master began to take an interest in his clever young slave. He loaned him books on philosophy and history, and Toussaint soaked up learning with avid thirst. He read the work of Epictetus, a white slave who lived in Roman times and who taught that mastery over oneself is the most important thing in life, whether one is slave or free. Since Toussaint had learned the art of self-mastery in overcoming his physical weakness, he took this stoic philosophy deeply to heart. He read Julius Caesar, and the great conqueror's lessons in military strategy took their place in the dark recesses of the young slave's mind alongside his knowledge of African bush warfare. He read the fiery, prophetic words of the

Abbé Raynal, who had visited the West Indies and had gone back to France to preach Revolution:

> Nations of Europe, your slaves need neither your generosity nor your advice to break the sacrilegious yoke which oppresses them. They need only a chief sufficiently courageous to lead them to vengeance and slaughter. Where is this great man to be found? He will appear, we cannot doubt it. He will show himself to raise the sacred standard of liberty and to gather round him his companions in misfortune! More impetuous than the mountain torrents, they will leave behind them on all sides the ineffaceable signs of their resentment! The old world as well as the new will applaud him. The name of the hero who will have reestablished the rights of the human species will be blessed forever.

The young boy who kept his thoughts to himself pondered long over these eloquent words. He had plenty of time to ponder. His master had made him keeper of the flocks and herds, and he spent days out on the hills with his quiet animals. He looked at the brooding mountains and the fair plains of his beautiful land, and thought about the imported, oppressed race of Africans who were almost ready to become its owners.

One day there was great excitement on the plantation. They had caught Macandal. He was to be burned at the stake in Cap François, Haiti's chief city, not far from Bréda. Every slave knew who Macandal was. He had made himself leader of hundreds of escaped slaves, called "Maroons," which means "wild hogs." These Maroons lived like Robin Hood's men in the high mountain forests. From time to time they would swoop down on the civilized plains, poisoning and pillaging, and keeping the white planters in a state of constant terror.

Macandal had made a plot to destroy the whites and take over Cap François. All the slaves knew this though they would have died rather than tell. He had arranged to have the sources of the city water poisoned. Then, while the whites were sick and dying, he and his Maroons, with the help of the Negroes in the city, would fall upon them. At the same time, according to his plan, the slaves were to rise on all the plantations of the North.

Like most bandits Macandal, while cruel, courageous and dangerous, was also impractical and foolhardy. A few days before this bloody revolt was to take place he went to a plantation dance, drank too much raw rum and started boasting about the great massacre that he, single-handed, had arranged.

Most slaves had a silent and deep agreement that they would never betray one another, even in the smallest things. Ordinarily the foolish Macandal would have been safe. But along with his rash boasting, the bandit flirted with a new and pretty slave girl. His own sweetheart saw this, and in a fit of jealous anger she told her white master the whole plot.

So Macandal was taken, and everyone who could get there, black as well as white, went to see him burned at the stake. This was an age of cruelty, and such bloody shows were considered entertainment. Instead of going to prize fights or wrestling matches to see two men pound or toss each other to a pulp, people would turn out in crowds to gape, scream or laugh at a hanging or a torturing.

Dainty, overdressed French ladies fanned themselves at their windows and chatted as the brigand was tied to the stake. Gorgeous mulatto women with towering,

As the flames mounted, Macandal struggled to break loose

brilliant-colored turbans, had themselves carried to the square in sedan chairs. They turned their smiling eyes now on their escorts, now on the horrible scene before them. Graceful black women with heavy baskets balanced on their heads paused to watch. Naked children screamed and ran between the legs of the crowd, sometimes falling into the filthy open gutters which ran through the centers of the streets. All the riffraff and all the elegance of the town were there, and a good sprinkling of slaves from the plantations, with their thoughts sewed up tightly in their heads.

Toussaint did not see the execution. He was gentle and humane, and all his life he hated violence. But he heard every detail of it as it was the sole topic of conversation for weeks afterward. He heard how Macandal, the flames already mounting around him, suddenly broke his bonds and ran shrieking across the square, all on fire. He heard how soldiers caught him and killed him immediately. But the slaves said that he had changed himself into a mosquito and escaped. Later he would take human form again and be a new leader.

This event made a tremendous impression on the thoughtful boy. He was horrified by it, but he wondered, too. Did courageous revolutionary spirit have to go hand in hand with brutality and recklessness? Could the slaves ever make a successful revolution without murdering and being murdered? Would they know how to govern themselves with a man like Macandal at their head? Must all the black leaders be like Macandal? Toussaint was never in his life a revolutionary at heart, but he began to understand both the need for revolution and the horrors of it.

The burning of Macandal was a symbol of the deep-seated hatred and fear between the blacks and the whites of Haiti. While Toussaint was growing up on the gracious and enlightened plantation of Bréda, other slaves—hundreds of thousands of them—were subject to tortures and degradation at the hands of cruel and frightened masters. And they retaliated with cunning, feigned stupidity or primitive revenge. The young boy heard the stories around the fires at night. When the slaves gathered after the long day's work, they threw off the sullen, sly manners with which they faced their white owners. They became vivacious, talkative and noisy. They told stories of their cleverness in outwitting their masters and laughed at them. But the stories were bitter, and the laughter was defiant.

A slave nurse, they said, angry at a whipping, had fed

a white baby an herb from the woods. In a few days his mouth was stuck shut, and he died for lack of food.

An old field hand was caught stealing potatoes and condemned to have his ear cut off. He had already lost one ear for an earlier small crime. When summoned before the executioner, he begged piteously,

"Master, please don't cut off my ear. I have only one left, and if I lose it, where am I going to keep my cigar?"

A white planter, who had spent twenty years building up a coffee plantation, was about to sell his crop and his slaves. This would bring him enough money to end his days in France. On the day before the gathering one of his slaves, seeking revenge for years of oppression, poisoned all the others. Since there were no laborers to gather the coffee, the crop was ruined and the planter had to start all over again.

Death meant little to the slaves, and revenge by killing or suicide was an everyday matter. According to his African beliefs, if a slave died he would wake up in Africa, and in any case he would be better off than he was in Haiti.

Young Toussaint listened to these boastful, bitter tales, and he forgave the slaves because he knew of the violence of their white masters. Punishments were frequent and severe out of all proportion to the crime. For the smallest offenses slaves were flogged to death with heavy whips made of plaited cowhide. Clever and hideous tortures were devised to kill rebellious slaves painfully. They were burned to death, blown up with gunpowder, partly buried in the ground with their bodies covered with molasses to attract ants, maimed by having an ear or even a hand cut off.

Even aside from punishments the life of the ordinary field slave was one long misery. Before dawn the cracking of whips and stifled groans and cries could be heard as slaves were driven into the fields. There they worked on the baked earth of the cane fields, which was so hard it often broke their hoes. At eight o'clock they were given a short stop for breakfast, then worked again until midday. After the midday rest they often worked until ten or eleven at night. They were not allowed to take a rest; the whips were always ready to prevent that.

Toussaint and his family lived in a roomy, well-built hut in the slave section of the plantation. Bréda cared well for its slaves, but it was exceptional. On most plantations the Negro huts were tiny, made of mud and wattles. No one ever repaired them, and the walls buckled and the roofs leaked. A whole family lived in a one-room hut with no windows, a dirt floor and one bed made of sagging cords. These wretched huts were built around a plot of land planted with vegetables, which the slaves were forced to till themselves in their free time. This saved their masters the expense of feeding them. Many of the slaves died slowly of starvation, too tired and listless at the end of the long day to cultivate their little plots.

The house slaves fared better, but they were subject to the fantastic whims of their indolent masters and

Toussaint and his family lived in a well-built hut in the slave section

mistresses. The slaves retaliated in their own ways, with slyness, shiftlessness and frequent secret violence, such as poisoning.

As Toussaint came to manhood, he watched the hatred and fear grow. He began to realize that they were reaching a boiling point. In the meantime his life ran a peaceful course in the midst of the rumbling volcano of his homeland. In his twenties he was made coachman, and the friendliness and trust between master and slave deepened. He continued to read everything his master gave him, and he listened to the stories of the other slaves. Steady, dependable, well-liked, both by his master and the plantation slaves, the quiet young man brooded silently over the injustices of his country and dreamed of his own destiny. Leaders are made in dangerous times, and it was not quite time for Toussaint. He waited, speaking little, smiling never, keeping his own counsel, already mysterious and already beloved.

2

The Unhappy Masters

HAITI WAS ALMOST READY FOR TOUSSAINT. ALTHOUGH the little French colony was the richest in the world, the system under which it was run had reached a point of rottenness where only revolution was possible. The white masters lived in a constant state of uneasy friction with one another and desperate fear of their slaves. This fear, in turn, led to excesses of cruelty and persecution.

Haiti had had a bloody and violent history. Three centuries before, in 1492, Columbus discovered the island. When his ship, the *Santa Maria*, was wrecked, the gentle Indians, who were the natives of the land, rescued him and his men and most of the stores on the ship. They showed the most hospitable kindness to the Spanish sailors, who they thought were gods. Columbus was enchanted.

"Haiti is the most beautiful thing in the world," he wrote. "In these delightful vales all the sweets of spring

21

are enjoyed without either winter or summer. Wherever we turn our eyes we are enchanted. Here I will dwell, I and my children, here I shall remain and the last remnant of my days be spent, and here I will be buried."

After betrayal and imprisonment, Columbus was buried in Haiti as he wished. The cruel Spanish conquerors who followed him lost no time in destroying the gentle, happy Indian population in their frenzied quest for gold. Castilian gentlemen used to find it a sport to go out shooting Indians. They would count it a bad day if they did not bag twelve, one for each Apostle. Deliberate famine, brutal overwork and wanton cruelty extinguished the Indians entirely.

The Spaniards were not good colonists. All they wanted was gold, and when they did not find it they grew lazy and shiftless. French buccaneers, operating from a nearby island, made an easy living capturing Spanish galleons and raiding the plains to catch the cattle that the lackadaisical Spanish had allowed to run wild. The buccaneers began settling on Haiti itself, and more and more Frenchmen came over to make a living in this beautiful and fertile land. In 1697, in a European war, France won half the island from the Spanish. Spain

"Wherever we turn our eyes we are enchanted," wrote Columbus

kept the eastern part of the island, which she called San Domingo. In the French part, which we now call Haiti, the practical and ambitious French began building a colony which was to astound the world with its wealth.

At first glance Haiti is inhospitable and forbidding. It looks as if a giant had crumpled a piece of dark green paper and thrown it down on the blue Caribbean Sea. It is a mass of tangled and folded mountains with deep, dark valleys running between them. But its new French owners found that this wild and desolate mountain country, near the size of Vermont, could be cultivated from its low marshy plains almost to the tops of the high mountains. They imported Africans, stronger and tougher than the Indians; and an ever-rising stream of sugar, cotton, indigo, coffee and cocoa came out of little Haiti. The profits rose fantastically every year. Nobody in eighteenth century Europe had ever seen anything like it.

The basis of the fabulous wealth was, of course, the inhuman system of slavery. Haiti had hundreds of thousands of African slaves, who suffered and died under the whips of their white masters to produce the wealth on which a few thousand Frenchmen grew rich.

To Europeans, Haiti sounded like a legend from the *Arabian Nights*. But the few travelers who ventured to this faraway island brought back reports of a life that was far from ideal. The inhabitants were ill at ease, decadent, cruel and fearful.

Who were these people who lived so unhappily in this earthly paradise?

When France got legal control of Haiti, she sent colonists to settle it and to tame the wild buccaneers. Many of these colonists were unfortunates from the prisons of France. They had gained their freedom by engaging themselves to work for a master for three years. Others were soldiers of fortune, second sons of impoverished noble families and down-at-the-heel adventurers who had failed at everything else. After them the French government sent women from the streets of Paris and women's prisons. These were the people who helped to populate the country, along with the buccaneers. Their children, born in Haiti, were called Creoles.

Though they were not French, the Creoles always regarded France as their native land, and longed to go there. In Haiti they had the temporary air of merchants at a fair, all in a constant hurry to be gone. Once a planter got to Paris he would show off with garish and vulgar wealth, entertain like an Oriental potentate and spend at least ten years' income in ten months. Then he would have to go back to his sinister and frightening country and start all over again. Nothing the Creoles did had any permanence, and the threat of Haiti hung over them like an evil pall.

The source of their fear was the slaves. As more and more slaves were brought in and prosperity grew to fantastic heights, the Creoles grew indolent, lawless and cruel. But they also grew frightened. By the time of the French Revolution, there were five hundred thousand slaves in Haiti and only forty thousand whites. Often a plantation deep in the country would be run by one white man and two hundred black slaves. The planters' fear of their own slaves led them to excesses of brutality and torture.

Plantations in the back country of Haiti, few and far separated, were run like armed fortresses. The plantation owners, among their hundreds of slaves, suffered from appalling loneliness and fear. Many of them built stone palisades in the mountains where they could flee in case the slaves started to revolt. They hardly knew their neighbors. If they did know them, they were either jealous of their fortunes or quarreled over boundaries and trespassing.

Around the plantation dwelling house the trees were usually cut down for firewood and building material, leaving the house ugly and bare to the blazing sun. Turkeys, ducks and hens ran wild over the grounds, laying their eggs anywhere, to be the prey of rats and snakes. The overseer paid no attention. He was too busy whipping the last ounce of work out of the slaves in the cane fields.

Inside the house the furniture, made crudely of native mahogany, was plain and heavy. The few lovely pieces of French furniture which found their way to Haiti would be chipped and stained. A beautifully inlaid rosewood desk would have before it a bench made out of a box. A crystal chandelier designed for two dozen candles would hold six melted stubs. Cobwebs were everywhere. Through the half-closed lattices came wind, sun, dust, rain and ants. The ants were so bad that they even got into the ink, and food had to be kept in drawers on legs resting in little troughs filled with water. At night the lattices were thrown open to let in the cooling night breeze. They also let in clouds of beetles, mosquitoes and moths, attracted by the candles which were the only lights. People kept lizards as pets because they were so good at destroying insects.

The food was coarse, though it was often eaten off solid gold plates. Many houses had no kitchens, and the food was cooked over a fire in the open air. Anyone who had a kitchen separated it from the main house because the kitchen slaves were so negligent and so dirty. The family coach would be gaudily decorated with gold leaf. But it would be drawn by horses and mules of different colors and sizes and with filthy harnesses and ropes for reins.

The typical lady of the manor had nothing to do but entertain herself. Sometimes she did a little cooking for fun; otherwise she had no household duties. She divided her time between her bath, her table and the ceremony of dressing and arranging her hair. If she read, it was a wicked, tasteless French novel. If, rarely, she visited in the city, she went to the theater and saw the coarsest melodrama. She was likely to be a beautiful creature, with skin like delicate ivory, untouched by rouge or powder, which would melt in the terrible heat. She had long, thick, glossy black hair. Her favorite oc-

As she lay in her hammock, her slave girls amused her

cupation was to lie in a hammock with one slave girl tickling the soles of her bare feet with a feather, while another sang her a coarse Creole song.

The lady's husband was usually dark and romantic-looking. Because there were no schools in Haiti, he had been sent to Paris when he was ten. There he had learned nothing that would fit him in any way for life as a planter in Haiti. When he inherited the plantation, he had the choice of staying in Paris as absentee owner, trusting his overseer to whip the slaves hard enough to keep the profits rising. Or he would come back, if he didn't trust the overseer, and do the job himself, hating it and waiting for the time when he would have collected enough money to visit what he still considered his homeland.

These white planters had nothing to talk about and no interest in life except their Negroes, their cotton, their sugar and their coffee. Most important was the number of Negroes. They reckoned wealth by Negroes instead of gold.

Their children were spoiled and completely free of any restraining influence. Unencumbered by the heavy swaddling clothes of European babies of that day, these Creole children learned to walk very young. From babyhood they lived mostly out of doors, barefooted and clad in the lightest of clothes. Riding, swimming and climbing came as naturally to them as to the little slave children. They grew up graceful, strong and lithe. Their easy life made them charming, courageous and open-handed. But they were also cruel, proud, quarrelsome and entirely unreliable. The earliest words they heard were the commands to whip their nurse. From the time they could talk, they had learned that a single word would bring a slave running.

"Bring me an egg!" a child would command.

"There are no eggs," the slave would reply.

"Then bring me *two* eggs!" the child would cry, stamping his foot in rage.

A capricious child who demanded this kind of unreasonable obedience was bound to grow into a cruel adult who ordered his slaves to accomplish impossible tasks and flogged them when they couldn't.

They did not stay children very long. A girl of fifteen would be married to a man three times her age. Still a child when she married, the girl would be totally uneducated, and as indolent and spoiled as her mother. Like her mother she would think only of her bath, her wardrobe, her table and her naughty French novels.

The uncomfortable, uneasy, fearful life of most of Haiti's planters was in great contrast to the life on Toussaint's Bréda plantation where all was beautiful and well-ordered. When Toussaint drove his mistress to town he traveled a straight, busy highway through the most civilized part of Haiti. Between the coffee plantations and the orange groves, palm-lined drives led to graceful plantation houses. There was a steady stream of travel: black women striding straight and free under the heavy loads balanced on their heads; children driving tiny, sturdy donkeys loaded with the bright-colored fruits of the tropics; creaking wagons drawn by mules, piled high with the household goods of poor white families; a few gaudily painted coaches like the one Toussaint drove.

Toussaint had an elegant uniform, but he was barefoot, for that was the mark of a slave. He sat proudly on his high coachman's seat, inclining his head when he passed friends on the road. Although he was a slave he had dignity and sureness as he handled the high-spirited horses.

In Cap François, usually called by the Haitians Le Cap, Toussaint took his mistress on a round of visiting. Le Cap was Haiti's loveliest and most civilized city. Its houses were built of stone covered with plaster, painted blue, pink, yellow or white, and fronted with galleries of delicate wrought iron. Its streets were straight and paved. To be sure, they were not paved very well. Puddles collected in them after a rain, and open sewers ran down the middle. But that was also true of most European cities in those days. There were two or three beautiful squares with fountains in them, usually dry because of defects in piping. Nothing in Haiti ever worked quite right. But in spite of its flaws Le Cap was a gracious and cultured city. Having the island's best harbor, and being the only place in Haiti that was free of earthquakes, it attracted travelers and merchants from all over the world. Americans had shops there; English soldiers and French sailors mingled in the taverns;

Toussaint sat proudly on his high coachman's seat

Creole ladies entertained European noblemen in their high-ceilinged, white-painted salons; there were balls and theater and music. And in the shopping center a lady could buy the latest fashions from Paris and the most expensive jewelry.

Between Bréda and Le Cap, Toussaint knew only the best part of Haiti. We have seen the discomfort of Hai-

ti's back-country plantations. Life in most of Haiti's cities was even more barbaric. Toussaint knew of it only
from hearsay as it was almost impossible to travel from
one city to another. There were few roads in the colony,
and these were never repaired. You could get from Port-
au-Prince to Jacmel, twenty-five miles away, only by a
winding, muddy lane that crossed the same river sixty-
five times, and never a bridge. But you had to do it
on horseback. A coach would break an axle on a rock or
tumble headlong down one of the steep precipices or
get stuck in the mud of the river. Almost everyone traveled on horseback on narrow trails through the dangerous, bandit-infested mountains, and on dusty tracks
over the lonely plains. A visitor coming by sea usually
landed at Le Cap. But some ships put in at Port-au-
Prince, which was actually the capital of Haiti. An
eighteenth century visitor landing at Port-au-Prince
has described his astonishment at what he found there.

He had expected the fabled city of golden wealth,
the throne of luxury, the center of the richest country
in the world. He saw instead two rows of huts, a rutted
mud track for a main street and a chaotic mass of wooden
barracks. It had rained in the night, and he came ashore
into a moist, hot, evil-smelling atmosphere. He could

hardly walk in the muddy street. Streams of water filled
the ditches at the sides of the street, and he heard the
croaking of toads.

Over the market place hung a sickening cloud of odors
of decaying fish and bad meat. Here there were two
fountains, the city's only water supply, around which
clustered a cackling, laughing, ever-changing crowd of
Negro women in colorless, shapeless dresses. They were
washing their dirty clothes, soaking manioc (a kind of
coarse grain), and making indigo. A merchant ran
down the street after a Negro, yelling that he had stolen
a pig. He caught the Negro and beat him unmercifully
with a cane while the pig ran away squealing. Nobody
even turned around.

The visitor wandered along the street examining the
buildings. There seemed to be nothing but theaters,
gambling dens and dance halls. He found one building
of stone, the governor's residence. Before it, was a little
esplanade with some spindly young trees and a Royal
Garden with almost no plants.

Port-au-Prince was much like the other cities of Haiti
except that it was a little bigger and a little dirtier.
The Haitians took no pride in their cities and seldom

tried to beautify them. After all, Paris was the only real city to them, even though most of them had never been there.

Toussaint did not know Port-au-Prince, but he knew the kind of people who lived there because the same kind lived in Le Cap, under its sprinkling of aristocrats and foreigners. These were the "little whites"—artisans, tradesmen, gamblers, riffraff of all sorts, eking out a precarious living. These people had little skill and less money. The doctors were generally half-trained surgeon's assistants from France who knew nothing about healing when they arrived in Haiti and refused to learn the use of native herbs. The masons were mostly day laborers who set themselves up in business with a couple of slaves, bought with money borrowed from a rich mulatto. A barber would have four slaves working together on a customer while he stood by twirling his cane, ready to strike any one of them at the smallest slip.

None of these "little whites" would be a servant, nor would he lift a finger to do anything that he could get a Negro to do for him. Owning nothing, they fed their pride on race prejudice. Their white skin was the most important thing in life to them, since it was all they had to make them feel superior to the wealthy mulattoes from whom they had to borrow money.

Toussaint knew these "little whites," because he often had to deal with them on shopping errands for his master. He responded to their open contempt with silent dignity. A slave must never answer back. And in any case he was not concerned with the gibes of men who were so obviously his inferiors. The insults that hurt the proud slave the most were those of the mulattoes.

Next to the slaves the mulattoes were the angriest and most unhappy people in Haiti. Part white and part Negro, they were as numerous as the whites in Haiti, and were considered a constant menace to white superiority. They lived in a half-world, no longer slaves, but not quite free men, suffering under the unremitting persecution of their white fathers. If a mulatto invited a white man to dinner, he would have to stand and watch his guest eat as mulattoes were not allowed to sit down to dinner with white men. He had to call the white man "Monsieur," even if the white were poor as a church mouse and the mulatto rich as Croesus. He was not al-

lowed to play European games, nor wear European
clothes, nor carry a sword. He could not gather with his
friends for a dance or a wedding, nor hold an office. So
the mulattoes, like downtrodden people everywhere,
worked extremely hard, and many of them got very rich.
About all they were allowed to do was lend money. This
they did to such an extent that practically every white
man in the colony was in debt to them. Naturally the
whites hated their creditors.

There were 128 shades of color listed for mulattoes,
with such fanciful names as "quarteron, sacatra, mar-
abou." If a woman was 127 parts white and one part
Negro she was still considered tainted, and no white man
could marry her. However these mulatto women were
usually charming. They danced gracefully and dressed
beautifully, and they made the white women very jealous. Once the white women of Le Cap went so far as to
force the passing of a decree that no mulatto could enter
a shop. Within a few days Le Cap's merchants were in
an uproar, and the decree was revoked. The rich, beautiful mulatto women were their best customers.

The mulattoes had wealth and polish. Their sons were
sent to schools in Paris, joined the best French regiments
and were even pages at court. They considered them-

selves the equals, if not the superiors, of most of the whites in Haiti. But the whites treated them like the scum of the earth. The mulattoes could not bring themselves to join with the Negroes, whom *they* considered the scum of the earth. They were too close to being slaves themselves to relish any reminder of it. It is said that they treated their slaves even more cruelly than the white planters did.

Toussaint burned with anger at the indignities inflicted on black slaves by the men who were their own brothers. Later on, as a leader, he was to have more trouble with the proud, narrow-minded mulattoes than with any of the white classes of Haiti.

Haiti was ruled by an inefficient, despotic and corrupt government, which did nothing to soothe the animosities of planters, little whites and mulattoes. At its head were a governor and an "intendant," both sent from France, who shared the running of the country. These two quarreled constantly as neither had enough power to overrule the other. Both were hated by the colonists because they were arbitrary and irresponsible. They could arrest without warrant, grant favors, increase taxes, confiscate property, and no one in the colony could say anything against it. The governor was usually a penniless grandee who had got his job through influence. He would stay in Haiti no more than two or three years, and then go back to France, having made his fortune for life. The hundreds of tax collectors made a good living accepting bribes from rich planters who did not want to be jailed for nonpayment of the high taxes. Justice was entirely a matter of how rich you were and whom you knew.

It was a disorderly, pretentious, opulent and wretched country that Toussaint saw around him. Way beneath all the quarreling, hating, fearing people lay the true source of all the wealth and all the corruption. This was the seething mass of African slaves, tortured, worked to death, desperately feared and entirely misunderstood.

3

"Pieces of the Indies"

TOUSSAINT UNDERSTOOD THE SLAVES, HIS OWN FELLOW creatures, and loved them and pitied them. Though he had been born in Haiti, and had had an easy childhood, his own father had been captured in Africa and brought to the New World in a slave ship. From his father and from the new slaves who were constantly being brought in, Toussaint learned of the hideous barbarity of the slave trade.

The slaves felt the first bite of the whip far away in the dense, low country of West Africa, many months before they were shipped to Haiti. From the day of their capture they were subject to torture and humiliation.

Picture a long line of blacks, chained together, marching wearily through the swampy jungles. Each one carried a heavy load of stones fastened on his back to prevent any attempts at escape. The Africans were driven by a few tired, angry-looking white men who whipped them up when they fell. If they could not rise, they were unchained and left lying by the trail to die in the wilderness. If they survived to reach the coast after many days and several hundred miles of traveling, they were crowded into small pens. There, packed tightly together, they were looked over by European buyers. The Europeans could not stay in the fetid pens for more than fifteen minutes. But the Africans had to, and many of them died there.

While the slaves were parceled out among the buyers, the captains waited peacefully on their ships in the African harbor. One of them actually composed a hymn, "How Sweet the Name of Jesus Sounds," while waiting for his human cargo. Slaving was no more than a business to the ship captains—not a very pleasant one, but highly lucrative. The slaves were reckoned, not as people, but as artificial units of height and weight, known in the trade as "pieces of the Indies." Shipowners were paid according to how many "pieces of the Indies" their ships would hold.

On the ships each slave was given a tiny space, too small for him either to sit up or lie down straight. There he was chained, right hand to right leg, left hand to left leg. Once a day all the slaves were unchained and pushed up on deck, where they were forced to dance for exercise. Many of them seized the opportunity to jump overboard. When the weather was bad, or when the slaves threatened revolt, as they often did, they were kept below for weeks at a time. There many of them died. The slaves were angry and proud and miserable, and they showed it. They broke their chains, went on hunger strikes and fought the sailors. About half of them never lived to see the West Indies.

The slaves that did arrive were examined by buyers at the slave market near the dock. They were pinched, prodded and poked. Their mouths were forced open so the buyers could see their teeth. When bought, they were branded on the chest with the owner's sign. The next step was the conversion to Christianity. With whips they were herded into church and forced to kneel. Words were chanted over them. Then the whips cracked again, and the slaves rose and went out. They were now Christians.

When they got to the plantations, the slaves were still not considered as human beings. Slaveholders figured out how long it would take a slave to pay for himself with labor—about seven years. During that time he was driven as hard as possible. If he were worn out or if he died at the end of seven years, it didn't matter. Another slave could be bought to take his place.

Among the slaves were priestesses and princesses and sons of chiefs (like Toussaint's father) who had been slaveholders themselves in the country of their birth. In the early days of the slave trade the African chiefs had sold the slavers inferior blacks who were already slaves. By the middle of the eighteenth century, how-ever, none of these unfortunates was left in Africa.

Tribes made war on one another and sold the cap-tives to the slavers. Chiefs sold their own wives and sons to save themselves. By the time of the French Revolution, probably more than half the slaves in the West Indies came from the upper classes in African tribal society. They brought with them their own gods and customs, their native African courtesy, their fierce pride, their vivacity and wit and love of dancing and singing.

Above all, they brought their extraordinary intelli-gence. The white man who bothered to study them found them to be as intelligent as any people he had ever known. Not allowed any education in Haiti, they educated one another in African lore. Thus they kept their spirit and their civilization alive in a hostile land. As many of them died under the whips and the brutal overwork, more were constantly brought in. In two and a half centuries twenty to thirty million slaves were brought to the New World. At the time of the French Revolution more than two-thirds of the slaves in Haiti had been born in Africa. They had acquired none of the docile manner of the blacks born in the new land. These African natives were dangerous. They were not used to being servants, and they hated their masters.

When Toussaint was about thirty years old, two things happened which affected him and his country deeply. The first was that his master made him steward of all the animals on the plantation and gave him charge of the instruments at the sugar refinery. This was a position which had always before been occupied by a white man. It immediately elevated Toussaint to a position of great respect among the other slaves—not only of Bréda, but of the neighboring plantations. Toussaint was now an acknowledged leader among the slaves, revered for his wisdom and for his skill with healing herbs, and loved for his gentle kindness.

The other event was the Revolution of the British

The rites were carried out at night deep in the forest (p. 49)

colonies of North America. It is not likely that Toussaint realized the significance of the American Revolution at once. But the spirit of revolution was in the air.

In the meantime, Toussaint's life was as peaceful and pleasant as life could be for a slave. He married a respectable, stout widow named Suzan. She was placid and good-natured, and they led a simple life in the midst of their chaotic homeland. They labored in their field together and always had enough food to give to the poorer Negroes. Churchgoing was a continual pleasure to them; and their family life, with two small sons, was quiet and content.

On Saturday evenings they often gathered with the

other slaves, who threw off their daytime masks of dull stupidity and talked, laughed and sang with noisy gaiety.

Their favorite dance was the wild, exciting *chica*. Everyone danced it, even the littlest children. They seemed to have been born knowing how to dance. The dancing was accompanied by two African drums covered with goatskin. One was long, the other short. One was beaten slowly, the other one fast, making a pulsating, hypnotic rhythm. With the firelight glowing on their dark, contorted bodies, and the sound of the weird, primitive chanting that accompanied the drums, a watcher might imagine he was in an African jungle. No doubt the slaves did, and that was one reason why they danced.

Toussaint knew there were often secret meetings in the woods, where the Africans practised their ancient rites. These rites were the only symbol of independence the slaves had. Consequently the whites were afraid and tried to discover who the priests were, in order to stop them. But the slaves were sullen and secret when whites were around. No one could tell by looking at a slave whether he was a priest or a common laborer.

The rites were carried out at night deep in the forest, and the slaves crept to their meeting places barefooted, using no torches. They knew the wild country as well at night as in the day, and their feet unerringly found the ancient trails first made by Indians centuries before. The white planters, shivering in their lonely houses, heard the distant drums, but they were helpless against them. Toussaint, as a moral Christian, hated and distrusted the African religion. He never attended these night meetings. Later on, when he became the most powerful and beloved leader in Haiti, he tried to stamp out the old rites. But even he could not stop them, and to a certain extent they are practised in Haiti to this day.

When the French Revolution came in 1789, Toussaint was about forty-five. The other slaves called him "Old Toussaint" because forty-five was old for a slave in Haiti. Most slaves died young, or were permanently disabled from overwork, beating and underfeeding long before they reached that age.

To his fellow slaves Toussaint was a paragon of knowledge and strength. He combined everything that was needed in a leader. He had the great physical skill and proud intelligence of the African native. He had a philosophic mind and perfect self-mastery, which gave him easy mastery over other people. As a slave he had learned, as all slaves must, how to deceive, how to flatter when necessary, how to hide his thoughts. As a slave, also, he had an understanding for lowly people. He knew how to joke with them and pray with them, and how to rouse their emotions with the simple, expressive language they understood.

His country was nearing the time of revolution—the time for Toussaint. The white and black races lived side by side uneasily. They were dependent on each other, but they walked in hate and terror. The more the whites beat and tortured their victims, the more rebellious and desperate the slaves became, particularly the new ones. There were many little revolts. There were mass suicides. As the whites yearned for Paris, so the slaves longed for the wide, free forest land of their fathers. This hopeless desire is described in a simple, touching scene described by a visiting Frenchman.

A slave leaned on the handle of his hoe, looking sadly out to the blue Caribbean Sea.

"What are you looking at, Nazimbo?" asked the visitor.

With tears in his eyes, the slave stretched out his hand toward the sea and said, "I see my own country."

"Poor slave," thought the stranger. "My country is out there too. I will see it again, but you will never see yours, Nazimbo."

But though the slaves often felt despair, they had unquenchable vitality. The will and ability for revolution were there. Only a spark was needed to set the destructive fires blazing all over Haiti.

"I see my own country," said the slave

4

The Black Hordes

ON AUGUST 22, 1791, HAITI BURST INTO THE FLAME OF revolution. At first not even the slaves knew what was happening. The revolution had started quietly and secretly, like a low fire deep in the woods which, unchecked, grows into an engulfing forest fire before anyone realizes its danger.

It really began two years before when the French people had risen against their king. The French Revolution had violent repercussions in Haiti. The planters got letters from France telling them of the atrocities of the peasants there. Castles were being burned, and the peasants were taking over the land and running it to suit themselves. The Haitian planters would gather in angry groups and talk over these horrors. Behind each planter's chair at dinner was a slave, silently taking in the conversation, to repeat it later around a fire in the woods. Sailors off the French ships, all ardent revo-

lutionaries, got drunk in the cities and chattered of
the great new age that was dawning in France. Slaves
heard the talk and brooded quietly over it.

No one paid any attention to what the slaves were
thinking. But the other people in Haiti thought that if
everyone in the mother country was to be free and equal
they ought to get something out of it, too. They began
quarreling fiercely among themselves.

Haiti finally reached such a dangerous state of conflict
that its government decided to use the despised and forgotten slaves in a move they hoped would end all the
quarreling at once. They would stage an uprising of
the slaves—just a little one, but enough to frighten everyone. They would arrange for many of the slaves to
walk off the plantations and hide in the woods. Then
they would call in a few French troops and pretend to
put down the pretended rebellion. The white population of Haiti, they thought, would be so grateful to
Mother France for averting this dreadful catastrophe
that there would be no more fighting and quarreling.

To accomplish this the government plotters called in
some of the Negro slaves who were leaders among their
own people. Toussaint was one of them. The government
proposed that these leaders should stage a small up-

rising. Knowing the power of the black leaders among the slaves, the government was sure that Toussaint and the others could keep the slaves in hand. In return for their cooperation, the black leaders were offered their freedom as well as a good sum of money. Some small reforms were promised for the great mass of the slaves— an additional free day a week and no more whipping. The black leaders agreed. Their first step was to arrange a slave meeting in the woods, where picked slaves would gather to be fired with the high purpose of revolt—but bloodless revolt.

The slave meeting was set for August 14, 1791. On that night the moon shone through a haze of mist on Haiti's towering shores. So bright was its light that an unearthly rainbow hovered over the huge blue-black mountains that came down almost to the ocean. To the sailors on a French frigate anchored in the harbor the place had a primeval, gloomy grandeur. There was not a light to be seen in the town. The steep mountain slopes, densely covered with trees, were so dark and silent that the watchers on the ship could almost think that the ghosts of the ancient Indians and their cruel Spanish conquerors alone walked the land.

They shouted and danced as a pig was sacrificed (*p. 58*)

A light breeze touched the ship, bringing a confused mixture of aromatic smells, the essence of the tropics. The city smells of filth and decay mingled with the heavy sweetness of acacia and orange blossom. Behind these was the faint coolness of the high pine forests. The land breeze also brought a sound which at first seemed to be the deep breathing of the island itself. It was the beating of distant drums, in an insistent, frightening rhythm. The sailors shivered on their safe ship.

In the heavy forest behind the coastal mountains, slaves were gathering in response to the drums. Silently, on bare feet, they stole from their plantations, just as they did when meeting for their religious rites. At a cleared space in the woods they crowded around a tall Negro tribal priest. He held his torch high, lighting up his long red robe and the intense, black faces around him.

The priest began speaking quietly, without anger. He told his audience that the French frigate anchored in the harbor held a letter from the French King promising reforms to the slaves. But the planters, he said, would not allow this letter to leave the ship, and guards were posted day and night to see that no one came ashore.

Then he raised his voice so that it echoed through the silent forest. Only the slaves, he cried, could help themselves, since no one else was going to help them.

Quiet again, he told them what they must do. In order to frighten the planters into honoring the King's reforms, the slaves were to walk off the plantations and hide in the woods until the planters were forced to grant the reforms. Their leaders on the plantations would tell them how and when to start, but—and here he was very deliberate—there must be no bloodshed and no violence.

Then the priest began chanting, working his followers into a fever of excitement. A pig was sacrificed and the slaves drank its blood, mixed with gunpowder, while they shouted an African oath against their enemies:

> *Bomba! Heu! Heu!*
> *Canga, bafio té!*
> *Canga, mouné de lé!*
> *Canga, do ki la!*
> *Canga, li!*

As the slaves chanted and danced, the priest raised his arms and intoned a war prayer:

"The god who created the sun which gives us light, who rouses the waves and rules the storm, though hidden in the clouds, he watches us. He sees all that the white man does. The god of the white man inspires him with crime, but our god directs us to do good works. Our god who is good to us orders us to revenge our wrongs. He will direct our arms and aid us. Throw away the symbol of the god of the whites who has so often caused us to weep, and listen to the voice of liberty, which speaks in the hearts of us all."

A week later, on August 22nd, at sunset, the slaves started leaving the plantations according to plan. In orderly fashion, they filed quietly from the fields and the houses. They carried their belongings in bundles and baskets on their heads. Brandishing his heavy whip, an overseer rushed out and ordered them to stop. The slaves simply looked at him in silent derision and went on their way. They were no longer afraid. Freedom was in their hands, and they quickly began to learn its strength. Yet they were quiet. There was no bloodshed, no looting.

The well-planned exodus continued into dark all over the great fertile plain of the North. The violence started when a few field hands on one of the larger plantations took advantage of their sudden freedom to settle some old scores. They stole around to the sugar house, found a young refiner's apprentice and hacked him to death with cutlasses. The overseer, hearing the screams, came running out with a pistol and was immediately cut down. The field hands suddenly went wild. They killed everyone they could find. Then they set fire to the sugar house. The acrid smell of burning sugar filled the plantation, and a viscous stream of molten sugar flowed over the yard. Through this the slaves slipped and stumbled, shouting wildly, brandishing torches and cutlasses and setting fire to the other outbuildings. One of them ran into the cane field and put his torch to the sugar cane. It caught quickly, and fire raged across the field.

The long line of slaves streaming quietly from neighboring plantations saw the red glow. Coming nearer, some of them saw the black figures scurrying around the plantation house, and heard the exultant shouts. They looked at each other, and suddenly the years of cruelty and oppresson rose around them like a cloud. It obscured everything but the immediate thirst for vengeance. Within a few hours fires raged over the whole northern plain. Many of the terrified white inhabitants fled into the woods or were murdered before they could escape.

The staged uprising was completely out of hand.

When the slaves began running wild, the city of Le Cap, on the edge of the northern plain, was in terror. Defenses were hastily thrown up. Women and children were herded onto the boats in the harbor. From there they watched the continuous rain of burning cane straw over the city. They saw black clouds of ashes over the fertile plains and flames rising fitfully from the fired plantation houses. Everyone who could bear arms in the city was pressed into military service. Cannons were mounted on boats lashed together in the river which formed one boundary of the city. The other entrance was a steep, mountainous pass which was guarded day and night.

There was also fear of the city's mulattoes. On which side would they fight? But the mulattoes were the first to volunteer to kill their black brothers, leaving their wives and children as hostages with the whites.

The French and mulatto soldiers went out from Le Cap on sorties, ranging over the burning cane fields. But for every slave they killed, two or three more sprang up to take his place.

"What are they fighting for?" the soldiers asked one another. "When you ask them why, they say the Rights of Man, or three days holiday a week with pay. They don't know themselves why they are fighting."

"They say they will do without masters, since the white slaves in France have decided to do without lords."

The Negroes might not have known what they were fighting for in precise political terms. But they fought with desperate courage to keep the freedom which they

A few field hands on one of the larger plantations settled some old scores

now tasted for the first time. They were an irresistible horde. They charged bayonets without fear. They caught the horses of the dragoons and pulled off the riders. They put their arms down the mouths of cannons to pull out the cannon balls. They swarmed over the gunners, chanting, just before the guns went off:

Gunpowder is but water!
Ping! Pandang!
Cannon is but bamboo!
Ping! Pandang!

They were not afraid of death. For they knew that if they died they would wake up in Africa.

In a frenzy of fear, the white planters killed every slave they could lay their hands on, even faithful house slaves. The result was that more and more slaves streamed into the woods to join the uprising. They brought silks and brocades, uniforms and medals looted from their masters' wardrobes, and every weapon they could find: heavy, ornamented swords, pitchforks, jeweled daggers, rusty old pistols, spades, knobbed wooden clubs. They made their ragged camp in the high mountain forests. From there they ranged down to the plains in their fantastic bits of uniform, carrying their awkward weapons, and taught lessons in courage to the cocky French soldiers.

Within a few weeks one hundred thousand slaves were in open revolt. The whole plain of the North was a smoking ash heap, and the white planters were calling desperately for aid from France. Suddenly the eyes of all Europe were focused on rich little Haiti, the Pearl of the Antilles. Her slaves were threatening the main source of French wealth, as well as the safety of all the other European possessions in the West.

5

The Old Slave Takes Over

TOUSSAINT STOOD BEFORE HIS MASTER AT THE BRÉDA
plantation. His crinkly hair was sprinkled with gray.
His eyes were slightly protruding; his lips were large
and thick; his small, lean figure was misshapen. When
he spoke he had a noticeable speech defect. He stood
there, not humbly, but with a commanding dignity and
sureness. His eyes were like steel though his voice was
gentle.

"I am taking the family away from Bréda," his master
was saying. "No plantation is safe against the rebels. I
have already instructed Madam to pack her belongings. You will take her and the children to Le Cap
within the hour."

"Master," said Toussaint quietly, "how little you
know Toussaint. You can not be safer anywhere than
you are at Bréda. The slaves obey my orders, and even

the rebels will respect the place where I am. I promise this before God."

It was true. The rebel slaves respected Toussaint's plantation, and for a while the black leader stayed away from the rebellion. Although he had helped to organize the bloodless uprising, Toussaint had regarded it solely as a method of gaining some reforms for the slaves. He had not envisaged this disorganized holocaust of fire and murder, and he distrusted it. It reminded him too much of Macandal and his bloody bandits. This would not gain the slaves reforms, he thought, but would only make their lot worse, once they were reduced to submission. Caution held him back; at any moment the ragged, aimless rebellion might be quelled.

It was not quelled, however, but grew to tremendous proportions. The white colonists saw to that. By murdering every slave they could catch, usually with fiendish tortures, they succeeded in alienating the entire black population, and driving thousands of desperate, frightened slaves to the rebel camp.

Toussaint began to see that what had started as an aimless revolt might, under careful leadership, be turned into a true revolution. He understood finally that it was time to declare himself. He told his master

The rebel leaders looked on Toussaint with scorn

and made thorough preparations for the white family's departure. He collected a large amount of sugar, which he sold, giving the sale money to his master. Then his brother drove the family to Le Cap, where he saw them safely embarked on a ship to the United States.

After he had said good-bye to his master, Toussaint got on his horse and rode to the rebel camp in the hills. He was received with a great lack of enthusiasm. The rebel leaders looked on him as a mild and overly cautious man, who was entirely too pleasant to white planters. They swaggered around the camp in stolen finery, covered with medals and orders. They gave themselves such resounding titles as "Generalissimo of the Conquered Territories," and surrounded themselves with royally uniformed bodyguards. Bloody revenge was their first thought, loot and riches their second. Beyond that, nothing.

"Oh, my friends!" one of them would cry after a murdering foray on the plantations. "How sweet, how good, this white blood! Let us take full draughts. Let us swear irreconcilable revenge against our oppressors. Peace with them never—so help me God!"

They cared nothing for the desperate, terrified mass of the rebels. In fact they took many of the Negroes, whom they called "rebellious," and sold them across the border to the Spanish for slaves. This gave them money to buy more ammunition.

Toussaint put on no fine uniform, spoke no fiery words. At Bréda he had been known as a healer. Now the rebel leaders, recognizing his skill and his popularity with many of the slaves, made him the medical officer of the camp. He set himself to curing the illnesses and binding the wounds of the black soldiers. He spoke to them quietly in their native African tongues, and listened to their stories. In a short time he was the most popular man in the camp. The other leaders began to listen to Toussaint's advice on military strategy. Most of them were totally uneducated, and Toussaint's knowledge and wisdom awed them. Soon he was admitted to equality as a military leader. In a few months he was recognized as the leading black general.

In the meantime, the colonists had got military aid from France to put down the revolt. But, haughty and intolerant, they did everything they could to hinder the French soldiers. The little whites refused to serve under mulatto generals. The planters wouldn't give an inch of concession to get their slaves back. The colonists continued to fight with the French government representatives. As a result the unhappy soldiers had to chase elusive blacks and at the same time keep the whites from cutting each other's throats. They went out on one hopeless sortie after another. They would come back discouraged, with half their number gone, and wonder what they were fighting about.

The rebel slaves were not well off either. They had burned the whole plain of the North and had nothing to eat. They couldn't get ammunition, and they weren't well enough trained to defeat the white soldiers in a decisive battle. The slaves starved up in the hills while the whites trembled down in the cities.

Toussaint, still cautious, always preferring peace to war and gradual reform to bloody revolution, decided it was time to make peace. He and the other rebel leaders made the colonists an offer of mildness and compromise: grant the slaves three days a week holiday with pay, abolish the whip and give freedom to four hundred Negro leaders.

But the stiff-necked colonists just pretended they hadn't heard. They still didn't take the rebellion seriously. Just send into the mountains a few really seasoned French troops, they thought, and the slaves would come crawling back on their hands and knees.

Toussaint was a man who knew when to compromise, and who usually preferred compromise to bloodshed. But he also knew at what point compromise became impossible. The slave revolt, he saw, had reached that point. The colonists sent back their final, contemptuous "No!" to his mild proposals. Then Toussaint realized that, if the slaves gave in now, they would go back to an oppression far worse than had existed before the rebellion. He came to a momentous decision.

He and his people would demand absolute freedom of the slaves as the price of peace. He knew that this would mean a fight to the death with the proud, spoiled colonists. But from now on, he saw, there was only one way the blacks could live as human beings in Haiti— that was as free men.

This was a great moment in history. In his decision to oppose slavery altogether Toussaint was far ahead of his time. Not until seventy years later were slaves in the United States freed. Back in 1791 slaves were slaves. That was the way it had been, and people thought that was the way it would always be.

"We have not brought half a million slaves from the coasts of Africa to make them into French citizens," said the colonists haughtily.

But Toussaint's decision put new life into his starving and discouraged band. Overnight a disorganized rebellion became a fight with a purpose, the highest of all purposes—freedom and equality for all.

For two years Toussaint trained a high-hearted little army in guerilla warfare while the colonists fought among themselves and disagreed on a method to end the slave revolt. By 1793, however, many of the starving rebel slaves had drifted back to bondage. Toussaint had a few picked men entirely devoted to him, but with one determined thrust by the French his small army would have been finished. This final thrust was being prepared when suddenly something happened in France which changed everything in Haiti and gave the rebels a fighting chance. King Louis XVI was removed from the throne and later guillotined. The French people took the government into their own hands with revolutionary enthusiasm, and France became a republic.

The rest of Europe was aghast and outraged. Armies were quickly mobilized for an attack on the upstart democracy in France which threatened the safety of royalty all over the world.

England and Spain, arming against France, thought smugly to themselves: here is our chance to get hold of Haiti, the Pearl of the Antilles. They both organized expeditionary forces for Haiti. The meager French army in Haiti saw itself faced with a war on two sides. England was approaching from the sea, and Spain from its own adjoining colony of San Domingo. The French in Haiti forgot all about Toussaint and his starving blacks up in the mountains, and quickly prepared a makeshift defense.

Toussaint and the other black leaders had two choices. They could lead the ragged, untrained slaves to the side of the weak new French democracy. That would mean sure defeat. Or they could join the Spanish and help them to fight the French. Like almost everyone else, Toussaint thought the French had no chance against the combined might of Europe.

However, if he joined the Spanish, he would be well supplied with weapons and ammunition. He would have time to train his own black army, and he could await his chance, which he was sure would come, to take over Haiti for the blacks.

Toussaint had only one burning purpose now—
the freedom of the slaves. So far as he could see, one
white man was much like another in his attitude toward
slavery, whether democrat or royalist, French or Spanish. But by joining the Spanish, he could save his slaves
from annihilation and train them for a better day.

As soon as he had allied himself and his band with
the Spanish, he proposed to his new allies that they
should announce emancipation in Haiti. That, said
Toussaint, would bring the four hundred thousand
slaves in Haiti to the Spanish side, and the small
white French population would be overrun immediately. The Spaniards threw up their hands in horror at
such a suggestion. But Toussaint did not forget his purpose, even though he fought under the Spanish king.
He wrote proclamations to the slaves of Haiti and invited them to join him in the fight for liberty. And he
began to build a real army.

In the beginning he trained the slaves in the African
bush warfare he had learned from his father. He taught
the black soldiers to gather themselves secretly into
small groups in the woods near a French encampment.
Out in the open priests chanted, and women and children danced themselves into a frenzy. When they had

become excited enough, the fighters would attack, rush up to the cannons and swarm over the gunners. If they met with stiff resistance, they disappeared into the woods silently and as if by magic. But the French soldiers, accustomed to conventional battle on an open field, were usually overcome with confusion and fled.

Toussaint knew that these bush tactics, though demoralizing to the enemy, would not win battles. He needed the arts of modern European warfare. White royalist soldiers and officers were deserting the French army in Haiti and offering their services to the Spanish. They feared and disliked the French Revolution, and they turned against their own country rather than join the new democracy.

Because the Spanish had few good fighting men, they relied on Toussaint and his blacks, who knew the country, to do their fighting for them. So, having no other choice, the deserting French officers volunteered to serve under Toussaint and the other black generals. They offered to help train the black army. Toussaint's soldiers, when they captured cannons, did not even know how to use them. Often they tried to fire the wrong end. The white officers taught them the use of artillery, and the new black army began to learn precision drilling, military discipline and the use of cavalry to supplement the work of foot soldiers.

Toussaint knew that with his savage crew iron discipline was necessary, and he instituted severe penalties for needless cruelty. He saw what had happened to his country under the senseless brutalities of the white colonists. He wanted to build a new kind of country, where his people would show themselves worthy of liberty.

The prisoners captured by his blacks were never killed or tortured but were treated with careful courtesy. When the black soldiers entered a town after a campaign in which they had had almost nothing to eat, they would not touch any of the town's provisions. To the frightened whites these half-naked soldiers, carrying makeshift weapons, looked like a barbaric Day of Judgment. But the African soldiers treated the inhabitants with mild politeness and trembled before their own officers.

More and more Haitian whites began to look to Toussaint for leadership. He was humane, and he never let vengeance interfere with good sense. The white colonists found they were better off if they joined him than if they tried to fight him. The weak French army offered them little protection, and the other black leaders were bloodthirsty.

In a short time Toussaint had developed an expert little army. His men adored him. He would ride with them on a long march, dressed in a simple field uniform, a yellow handkerchief knotted around his head. He would gallop up and down the line, joking, chatting and even praying with them. When they came to a stream, he would stand on his horse and give a wild whoop as the horse leaped into the water. If he fell in, as he sometimes did, he would laugh as loudly as they did. He led battle charges, taking daredevil risks. In one battle he chased the enemy commander alone for more than a mile and came back with two prisoners. He was wounded many times but escaped death by a seeming miracle. The black soldiers began to look on him as a sort of deity, whom mere bullets could never kill.

The blacks led a hard life in Toussaint's army, but they were used to hard living. They much preferred the army to the cruel and degrading life they had led as slaves in the field. If there was nothing to eat, they could live on bananas, sour oranges, herbs and roots. They could lie down and sleep in the cold, wet woods, and could march many hours almost naked and not be hurt by the burning sun. They were wise in the ways of their own country.

Toussaint's officers, fierce and ungovernable men, were more difficult to control than his common soldiers. But they bowed before his extraordinary ability, the sharpness of his tongue and the steeliness of his black eyes. They all feared him. Gradually they, too, began to worship him.

During the time that he fought with the Spanish, Toussaint adopted the name Louverture, which means "opening." Some say the name comes from the exclamation of one of the French generals: "This man makes an opening wherever he goes!" Others say that the blacks gave Toussaint the name because he opened the gate of freedom for them.

In a surprisingly short time Toussaint had most of North Haiti under his control, in the name of the Spanish. The British held a large part of the West and most of the important harbors. The poor weak French were at their wits' end. In spite of their critical situation they were still fighting among themselves. The French revolutionary government had sent over an able man named Sonthonax, of strong democratic sympathies.

His job was to unite the French colonists and try to put up some sort of capable resistance. At the same time, the government sent a new governor, an aristocrat named Galbaud. Galbaud and Sonthonax immediately fell into the same endless quarreling.

Then suddenly Sonthonax, forced by Galbaud's threats, made an unprecedented and historic move. On June 24, 1793, at Bréda plantation, where Toussaint was born, he announced that any slave who would join with him against the reactionary Galbaud would be a free French citizen forever after. As at a signal ten thousand blacks swooped down on Le Cap, burned two-thirds of the city to the ground, and drove out Galbaud and his reactionary forces. Galbaud fell into the harbor in his haste to get out of the city, and had to swim to a boat. Thousands of white Creole refuges piled onto every available boat in the harbor and set sail for the United States, where their descendants still live, in Virginia, Maryland, Pennsylvania and New England.

This was the end of white domination of Haiti and the first step toward complete emancipation.

But it was not a big enough step for Toussaint. He appreciated what Sonthonax had done, but he needed assurance that it would stay done. Haiti was, after all, still a French colony. Only from the French government could come a real law for the freedom of the slaves. At any moment Sonthonax might be recalled and his proclamation nullified. Toussaint stayed with the Spanish, who treated him well and seemed not to notice that he was black. He was still cautious, still biding his time.

The next step was more decisive. After guillotining their King the French people went through a period of intense revolutionary ardor. The masses were in a hysteria of fervor about freedom and equality, and they burned with indignation for the poor blacks of Haiti. They even refused to drink coffee because it was made with the blood and tears of their downtrodden black brothers. In January, 1794, two and a half years after the beginning of the revolt, the matter of freedom for the slaves finally came up in the revolutionary French assembly. A motion was introduced:

"When drawing up the constitution of the French people we paid no attention to the unhappy Negroes. Posterity will bear us a great reproach for that. Let us repair the wrong—let us proclaim the liberty of the Negroes. Mr. President, do not suffer the convention to dishonor itself by a discussion."

The slaves were officially free.

But the powerful merchants and slave traders grumbled, and in a short time the French would be sorry for their enthusiastic act.

In the meantime Toussaint had the chance he had been waiting for. He immediately offered his services to the friendly new French democracy. He and France were on the same side now. He had a fine little army of free men, already far superior to the weak French forces. He would use it to help the French drive out the foreign enemies. Then he and the French could cooperate to make Haiti a real democracy.

He had a tremendous job ahead of him. He had to defeat the English enemy, who held a large part of Haiti, and his erstwhile allies, the Spanish, who were a danger on the border. He had to bring back to life a country largely destroyed by fire and murder. He had to organize and educate hundreds of thousands of Africans who had no idea what freedom meant, beyond freedom to kill their masters and live off the land without working. He had to get rid of such representatives of the French government as might try to prevent the education of the blacks. At the same time he had to remain loyal to France. Toussaint had no wish to break with France so long as the mother country allowed the slaves to keep their freedom. Revolutionary France was, for the time being, his friend. It was also becoming a powerful state. Toussaint realized it would be dangerous to antagonize such a power.

He had very little time, and he knew it. To accomplish these superhuman tasks he had to be a military genius, a capable, firm, kind administrator, and a shrewd and wily diplomat. He was all of these, and he had no doubts about his abilities. The old slave had come into his own.

6

"There is Only One Toussaint"

LIKE LIGHTNING TOUSSAINT TURNED ON THE SPANISH who had been his allies. He bore them no ill will, and there was very little bloodshed as the few white Spanish soldiers fled before his speedy assault. With masterly diplomacy he persuaded most of the other black leaders to follow him even though they had been royalists. After three months a large and orderly black army was ready to come to the aid of French democracy in Haiti.

The first necessity was to drive out the British, and Toussaint jumped on them with characteristic speed. The black soldiers and the newly organized mulatto army succeeded in dislodging the enemy from most of the important points. But the stubborn British held out, refusing to give up the dream of adding rich little Haiti to the already monstrous British Empire. The British attempt to take Haiti and destroy the power of the French in the West Indies took five long years. It

84

was a disastrous war for England. In Haiti the British thought they would have to fight a few decadent white French planters and some dissatisfied slaves. But they found a whole population—black, mulatto and white—had risen solidly against them. For five years England's soldiers were killed by ex-slaves who loved their country and their liberty more than their lives. For five years English soldiers died by the thousand of yellow fever and other diseases of the tropics. And still England kept pouring them in. It was as if she threw her soldiers into a quicksand. They sank in the mires of Haiti. By the end of the war, England had practically no army left. Eighty thousand British soldiers had died or were unfit for further service.

When the Negro army finally entered Port-au-Prince in victory, Toussaint put on the first of the great triumphal shows with which he loved to delight his people. He was greeted at the city's gates by girls who threw flowers in his path. He dismounted and genuflected before the cross. A priest's canopy, or baldachin, was raised over his head while choirboys swung censers. But Toussaint stepped aside, frowning, and said, "It belongs only to God to walk under a baldachin and have incense wafted toward Him." He walked uncovered in the procession, in his simple general's uniform, his yellow handkerchief knotted around his head. Beside him was a guard of honor composed of the sons of wealthy planters. Behind him were white Creole ladies in their carriages, followed by the entire populace. At the church the most beautiful of the Creole ladies placed a laurel wreath on his head, and he kissed her. Then a salvo of twenty-two pieces of cannon boomed out to announce a Te Deum, and the whole company filed into church.

Though he was modest and deeply religious, Toussaint took an almost childish delight in these big spectacles, and never lost a chance to put one on. His people, he knew, loved the pomp and ritual as much as he did.

By the time the British were defeated, in 1798, Toussaint's word was law over most of Haiti. He had an army totally devoted to him, and he was rapidly gaining the blessings of the ex-slaves and the friendship of the whites. He was the one man who was able to reconcile the opposing desires of the lowest and highest classes in Haiti.

Even while the fiercest fighting was going on, Toussaint found time to soothe the troubles of the field laborers. These unhappy, bewildered, ignorant crea-

One of the Creole ladies placed a wreath upon his head

tures didn't yet know the meaning of freedom, and were easily misled. At the least hint that their former masters were trying to oppress them again they would rise and assassinate them and then run away. Toussaint pitied the confused blacks, but he was stern with them.

"Oh you Africans, my brothers!" he cried, as he came to a plantation torn by insurrection. "You who have cost me so much fatigue, so much labor, so much worry, you whose liberty is sealed with more than half your own blood! How long will I have the mortification of seeing my misled children fly the counsels of a father who idolizes them?"

"Alas, General," the leader of the blacks replied, "they want to make us slaves again. They look at us with a bad eye. They persecute us."

Toussaint called them all together and told them to work hard and be obedient. He appointed a military commander to see that they did not run away and that the white planters did not persecute them. He promised them a quarter of the produce. He was firm, but he was kind. The blacks danced and cheered him.

During the years of war Toussaint held out a hand of friendship to the white planters. He never trusted them, but he needed their knowledge, education and experience. He sent his troops, so recently half-naked, screaming savages, to collect the scattered planters and escort them with the utmost politeness back to their plantations. If they did not go, they would lose their property. Those who had fled the country began trickling back, hearing of Toussaint's mildness and the courtesy of his soldiers.

Stories of his forgiveness gave the whites confidence. Four Frenchmen, they heard, had deserted Toussaint's army with aggravated treachery. The deserters were caught, and everyone expected they would be promptly shot. Toussaint left them in suspense for a few days. Then on Sunday he ordered them to be produced in church. The priest reached the part of the service dealing with forgiveness. At that point Toussaint walked with the French deserters to the altar, gently pointed out their treachery and let them leave the church free men. By such means, the frightened, hostile whites were gradually reassured. As prosperity grew again under his careful, humane guidance, they too began to bless him.

Toussaint looked out for Haiti in another direction: he began to make friends with other countries. When the British had had enough of fighting in Haiti, they offered to make a secret treaty with Toussaint. In this treaty they would recognize him as king of Haiti, take away the rest of their soldiers from his country and sign a trade agreement with him. Toussaint agreed to all this except being made king. Personal power and resounding titles were never Toussaint's desires. His aim was the strength and unity of his country, and this, he saw, could be accomplished only if he remained friendly with democratic France. His country was not strong enough for the break which would come if he were declared king of an independent Haiti. And he doubted that the British would support a black slave if it came to a showdown. He knew how the British felt about slaves; most of their colonial wealth also rested on the slave system. But the trade agreement was valuable to him as he badly needed food and guns.

Toussaint made another secret trade agreement with the United States, which was the closest large country. It was natural for the two countries to carry on a brisk trade though the French had never allowed it.

Toussaint's most difficult problem in diplomacy was in dealing with the representatives of France, who still technically ruled the colony. Though Toussaint held the real power, he had to remain friendly with the French.

But they had a regrettable tendency to interfere with his work of uniting and educating his country.

The first French representative that Toussaint got rid of was a good old man, Laveaux, who was governor and commander-in-chief of Haiti during the war with the British. Toussaint had no personal quarrel with Laveaux; in fact they were close friends. Generally Toussaint was not a man who made friends. He held himself aloof, and people either adored him or feared him. Laveaux was probably the only close friend that Toussaint ever had outside his family. It was a strange friendship, that of the cultivated old aristocrat of one of the most civilized countries in the world, and the slave only one generation removed from Africa. But it was a true and trusting one on both sides. During the war Toussaint made continual reports to Laveaux, and asked the old man's advice on everything. He added friendly post-scripts to his letters.

"Here is something important," Toussaint wrote at the end of a military report. "I send you some truffles. Be so kind as to accept them from him who wishes you the best of health and who embraces you with all his heart."

But when the British were finally defeated Toussaint realized that the revolutionary pendulum was swinging back in France. The new dictatorial government in Paris had no liking for black slave upstarts, and the French merchants were muttering about the restoration of slavery. Toussaint had to make himself and his country stronger in order to be ready for the fight, which he knew would come, with the French. Laveaux was technically the ruler of Haiti. Much as he loved the old man, Toussaint knew that in the crisis Laveaux, as a patriotic white Frenchman, would put France before Haiti. To keep unity, the ruler of Haiti must be a black man.

To Toussaint, as an unswerving patriot, the freedom of his country was more important than his friendship with Laveaux. He wrote to Laveaux, suggesting his departure by tactfully naming him a representative for Haiti in the French government:

"Foreseeing (as I do with sorrow) that great unpleasantness is in store for you in this unhappy land, for whose welfare you have sacrificed health and family, I should like to see you elected to the French Assembly. This will give you the satisfaction of seeing your fatherland and your wife and children again. At the same time my comrades-in-arms and myself will have gained the advantage of being represented by the most devoted of advocates. Yes, my General, my Father, my benefactor, France has many excellent men, but where is the man who, like you, can be relied upon always to remain the true friend of the Blacks? No, your equal there will never be!"

Laveaux, it is true, was old and needed a rest. And, to his credit, he understood and sympathized with his friend's aims. Graciously he took the hint and went back to France. He and Toussaint continued to be good friends.

The next French representative was both more dangerous and more difficult to get rid of. This was Sonthonax, the French Commissioner who had first decreed emancipation and who was now back in Haiti busily making himself popular with the Negroes. He built schools, encouraged agriculture, distributed muskets to the field workers, and never ceased to point out that it was he who had first given the Negroes their freedom and that he was their real benefactor. The blacks worshiped him.

Sonthonax's first act, after the departure of Laveaux, was to make Toussaint governor and commander-in-chief. The old slave now held, with the official blessing of the French, the positions which for several years he had held in actual fact.

But Sonthonax intended to use Toussaint for his own aims. He knew that Toussaint was the undisputed leader of Haiti, but he underestimated the wise slave, regarding him as a half-educated barbarian, unfit to rule. Worse than that, he underestimated the Negroes, thinking them too stupid to understand the true meaning of freedom. The blacks, he assumed, would blindly follow any leader so long as he kept their worship. To them, he thought, a single man meant Fatherland and Freedom, and he wanted to be that one man, that absolute ruler. He would use Toussaint to accomplish this ambition. First he proposed to Toussaint that they should massacre the whites and rule Haiti together. In the back of his mind was the intention of getting rid of Toussaint as soon as the whites were annihilated.

Toussaint rejected Sonthonax's proposal indignantly. He had realized from the beginning that Sonthonax was the kind of revolutionary who becomes dangerous when he gets too much power. He was astute enough to recognize the dangers of extremism and violence, which were never his way. Sonthonax, he saw, could only bring ultimate disaster to his people.

Despite his popularity Sonthonax had to go. First Toussaint tried the same tactful method he had used with Laveaux. But Sonthonax refused to be a representative and go back to France. So Toussaint openly accused him of conspiracy against the white landowners. The Frenchman was given the choice of being put forcibly on a ship or going on his own initiative. He took the latter course, and Toussaint, always a good showman, saw that it was accomplished in style. Crowds lined the streets. In sorrowful silence the people watched Sonthonax go, removing their hats as he passed. At the dock, dragoons were lined up and raised their swords in salute. Toussaint said a respectful farewell, the guns of the fort fired a salute and the ship sailed.

The next representative from France was the haughty Marquis de Hédouville. Before he left France friends had warned him, "With Toussaint you can do all; without him you can do nothing."

"Nonsense," he boasted. "I could go into the camp of the old monkey with the handkerchief and capture him with four men."

Still Hédouville was too wary to defy Toussaint's power openly. In the beginning he restricted himself to verbal trickery. On his arrival he greeted Toussaint with a warm invitation to make a ceremonial visit to France in the ship which had brought the Marquis to Haiti.

Toussaint was no innocent barbarian open to flattery. He was a polished diplomat, and he knew exactly what a visit to France meant. "Sir," he said with calm dignity, "your ship is not big enough to hold me." He pointed to a sapling in the garden. "I will go when that tree has grown large enough to make a ship."

Hédouville disagreed with the wise leader on every move for the country's betterment. He became more and more open in his insults, and Toussaint finally saw that there was only one way to deal with Hédouville. He gathered his pride around him and wrote a note to the Marquis:

"Your constant reminders that it is in your power to dismiss me lead me to believe that you would very much like to do so." He thereupon retired to his plantation and watched quietly, while Hédouville brought ruin down on his head.

The Negroes would make sacrifices for their beloved Toussaint, but they wouldn't take anything from the contemptuous Hédouville. They rebelled at every suggestion. He made the final mistake of arresting Tous-

The French soldiers tumbled pell-mell into their ships

saint's nephew Moïse, one of the most popular of the black generals. At this Toussaint waited no longer. He instigated a popular uprising. His men went galloping through the land, shouting at every farm house:

"Hédouville wants to restore slavery! He is disbanding the Negro army! On to Le Cap!" The field hands poured on Le Cap by the thousand, and proud Hédouville and his boastful soldiers tumbled pell-mell into the ships. The old monkey with the handkerchief had proved too much for them.

Thus was another interfering Frenchman disposed of.

he next morning there was the usual Te Deum, with all the pomp and circumstance which Toussaint loved so well. When it was over he walked out into the square and mounted his favorite horse, the beautiful Bel-Argent. His face was grave as he spoke to his people sadly and quietly:

"I have learned too much of the human heart not to be convinced that it is only in the bosom of my family that I can find happiness. I am old and weary. I have decided to retire."

"No! No! No!" shouted the crowd. "Papa Toussaint, don't leave us!" People fell on their knees. Mothers held up their babies toward him. He stood silently and watched them. Finally he said:

"So be it. Since you demand it, I will make the sacrifice. God preserve you and our country." The cheers were deafening. He raised his arm for silence and spoke again, and this time he had a new, warlike tone.

"Hédouville says that I am against liberty, that I wanted to surrender to the English, that I wish to make myself independent. Who ought to love liberty more— Toussaint, slave of Bréda, or General Hédouville, former Marquis and Chevalier de Saint Louis? If I wished to surrender to the English, would I have chased them away? Hédouville has spread the rumor that he was going to France to raise an army and that he will return. He thinks he can frighten me. But remember, there is only one Toussaint in Haiti, and at his name everybody must tremble!"

Toussaint was a brilliant actor. He knew how to rouse his people to the last pitch of enthusiasm. But he never did it for the sake of personal power. Hédouville had shown himself to be an enemy to Toussaint's dream of a free, united Haiti. If Hédouville had remained, Haiti would have fallen into the same chaos of internal dissension that had torn her apart before the slave revolution. Toussaint had deliberately roused the people against him, defied and insulted him and forced him out of Haiti. In doing this he knew that he had also defied and insulted France. But the wise leader realized that the time for compromise with France and her officials was almost over. When Hédouville left, in 1799, the Revolution was finished in France. Toussaint knew it was only a matter of time before the French would come back to enslave his people again.

He needed every ounce of devotion he could win before the French would get around to trying to restore slavery. Most of this devotion came from the gentleness and humaneness of his wise rule. But sometimes, good leader that he was, he knew that the people needed the kind of dramatic and artful show he put on in Le Cap that day, when he asserted his defiance and his leadership in ringing tones.

But his country was not yet united. Toussaint still had monumental obstacles to overcome before Haiti would be ready to face the power of an aroused France.

7

The War of Knives

WAR WAS AN EVERYDAY MATTER IN HAITI. BUT THE worst of her wars was now, in 1799, about to start. At this time Toussaint's word was law over most of Haiti, among blacks and whites alike. But there was one large group which still held out against the black leader—the mulattoes. In the south of Haiti these proud, restless people were preparing to revolt against Toussaint.

The mulattoes thought they were the true heirs of Haiti. To realize this dream they had fought, now with the royalists, now with the Haitian government, even occasionally with the blacks, depending on which side seemed to have the advantage. They fought well and courageously and had a highly trained army under one of the best generals of Haiti, Rigaud. He was subject to Toussaint, but he chafed at being second.

Rigaud's father was a French nobleman, his mother a Haitian Negro. His father had sent the boy to school in

France, and he came back to Haiti restless and ambitious. Early in the Revolution he became a leader of the mulattoes. Under his expert soldiery the mulattoes had helped to drive the British from the southern part of Haiti. Rigaud and the mulattoes were now virtual rulers of South and West Haiti.

An adventurer at heart, Rigaud was small but handsome, and had a proud, dangerous look. He wore a straight brown wig to emphasize his white skin. But at heart he was a fanatical mulatto. In his army neither whites nor blacks were allowed to be officers. He wanted to establish mulatto rule over all Haiti, as he had done in his own territory.

Part of the evil that Hédouville had accomplished during his short stay in Haiti was to tempt Rigaud with dreams of grandeur. Toussaint must be removed from the supreme command, Hédouville had said, and who was better fitted to take it over than Rigaud? Hédouville's only purpose was to make trouble between the blacks and the mulattoes, thereby weakening the power of both. But Rigaud didn't know this. All he saw was the chance of which he had dreamed. He cast his lot with the false French against his black brothers.

He made forced loans and stole food from the helpless inhabitants to outfit his army. When he considered himself impregnable, he deliberately provoked Toussaint into war. His army was far better supplied than Toussaint's, but Toussaint had the country behind him, both blacks and whites. Toussaint might be gentle by nature, but when truly aroused he was fierce. This unnecessary war between brothers angered him more than anything that had happened in his country so far. He denounced the mulattoes passionately:

"You, who from the beginning of the Revolution have been betraying the blacks, what is it you want? Everybody knows what you want. You want to rule the colony. You want to exterminate the whites and subjugate the blacks. Consider well before you take the fatal step, you who have dishonored yourselves. As for Rigaud, he is lost. I can see him in my mind's eye at the bottom of the abyss. The hosts of liberty will crush him, the rebel and traitor! Mulattoes, I can see to the very bottom of your souls. You meant to revolt, but remember that even if my entire army were to depart from here my eye and my arm will remain—my eye to watch you, my arm to reach out for you."

The mulattoes did not have a chance against Toussaint and his freedom-loving, perfectly disciplined blacks. He chased them out of the West, he chased them out of the South. Finally he had the remainder of the mulatto army bottled up in Jacmel, a southern seaport. All this time he did not arrest Rigaud. Rigaud would have been an easy man to catch, for he spent a great deal of time carousing in the towns when he should have been out leading his men in the field.

"Why do you not arrest Rigaud and end the rebellion at one blow?" asked one of his officers.

Toussaint gave an honest and astute answer: "The mulatto caste is superior to my own. If I take Rigaud from them, they will find another better than he. I know Rigaud. He gives up the bridle when he gallops; he shows his arm when he strikes. For me, I gallop also, but I know where to stop. And when I strike I am felt, not seen. Monsieur Rigaud can conduct insurrections only by blood and massacres. I know how to put the people in motion, but when I appear, all must be tranquil."

Jacmel was a pretty little seaport nestling amid palms and acacias in a circle of mountains strong enough to resist attack. This natural fortress had a small harbor and the most beautiful beach in Haiti. It was easily accessi-

ble by sea, but Toussaint had no ships. He had to lay
siege to the town. Jacmel put up one of the most heroic
defenses in all the history of wars.

The mulattoes had found themselves a leader better
than Rigaud. This was Pétion, who was many years later
to be the ruler of an independent Haiti. While Rigaud
waited indecisively for help from France which never
came, Pétion inspired the courage of desperation in his
little stronghold.

For five months Jacmel resisted. After a while there
was no food left; the inhabitants ate horses, dogs, cats,
rats, lizards. Leaves and grass were considered a deli-
cacy. When lead and cannon balls gave out, they put
rocks and pebbles into their cannons and fired them.
Finally there was no gunpowder left, and Pétion realized that his men could hold out no longer. But he
would not surrender. He tore the flags down from the
staffs and commanded the men to bind strips of them
around their bodies. Thus, if they perished, they would
still be faithful to their colors. Then he led them out of
the town, and they cut their way through the besieging
army with terrible losses.

The war was virtually over. But it had a long, bitter
ending. Rigaud, his ambition turning sour within him,

They threw away their muskets and fought with knives

refused to surrender. He gathered around him the few hundred devoted soldiers who had stayed by him and ordered:

"Lay waste the country, my soldiers, until the trees shall have their roots in the air."

Bands of marauders spread blood and terror. When small groups of soldiers met in battle, they would throw away their muskets and fight with knives, cutting each other's throats and tearing each other with their teeth. For many generations, this was known as the "War of

Knives." As in our own Civil War, the hatred was all the more fierce because it was between brothers.

Finally the last desperate marauders were subdued, and the war was over. Toussaint sent Vincent, the most trusted of his white generals, to arrange a truce with Rigaud. Into a small conference room where Vincent awaited him, the defeated general strode ferociously. He wore a green uniform without insignia of rank. He had a huge sword at his side and pistols in his belt. In his hand he held an unsheathed dagger with the blade hidden in his sleeve. He advanced on Vincent so fiercely that the white general feared for his life. But Rigaud only raved and ranted against Toussaint. He would sign no truce. He would not see Toussaint. Turning nervous and despondent, he shouted that he would kill himself. Suddenly he got up and stormed out. Rigaud was betrayed, defeated, finished, and he couldn't stand it.

The next day he sailed for France. Once he had reached Paris he went to see Napoleon, who had come into power while civil war was going on in Haiti. Napoleon had watched its progress carefully, but he had not intervened on either side. The French government, in fact, had been happy to see the slaughter and bitterness in Haiti. It hoped that both sides would destroy each other.

Napoleon received the angry Rigaud, but offered him no comfort. He looked the mulatto general sternly in the eye and said, "General, I blame you for only one thing—not to have been victorious."

In Haiti Toussaint set about to pacify the South and West. He quickly gained the admiration of the mulattoes by his forgiveness. He did not confiscate the property of those who had fought against him, but gave one-quarter of the produce to the laborers and one-half to the public treasury. One-quarter was to be saved for the owners in case they returned. But he made one mistake, and it took the mulattoes a long time to forgive him for it. He put in charge of the province the most terrible —but also the most brilliant—of his generals. This was the savage Dessalines, who later betrayed Toussaint, and still later named himself emperor of Haiti. Toussaint ordered Dessalines to purge the mulatto troops. Dessalines, given a free hand, went to work with fervor. His murdering went to such terrible lengths that Toussaint, outraged, put a stop to it.

"I said to prune the tree," said Toussaint sternly, "not

to uproot it." The murdering stopped, but bitterness remained. The mulattoes were not yet won over.

By 1800 Toussaint was governor of all Haiti. But he had one more war to make before his country would be strong enough to resist the inevitable French troops. A short time before Spain had ceded her part of the island, San Domingo, to France. The French had done nothing about taking over its government. Toussaint realized that as long as French troops could land in Spanish San Domingo and pour over the border, his country could never be safe. He resolved, therefore, to take over San Domingo. He would do it in the name of France. But when he sought the needed authorization from the French Commissioner in Haiti, a man named Roume, it was curtly refused.

Using the tactics which were always immediately effective, Toussaint roused the field hands. They marched on Le Cap. With a great show of fury and violence, they seized Roume and held a sword over his head.

Roume stood his ground valiantly. "Strike! France will avenge me!" he shouted.

But Toussaint wanted no heroic French martyr. He gave orders that Roume was not to be hurt, and the indignant Frenchman found himself locked in a chicken coop overnight. There Toussaint confronted him the next morning. The Negro leader said that he could no longer hold back the mob unless Roume gave him the authorization he needed. Furious, Roume signed it.

Toussaint now wrote to the Spanish governor and ordered him to surrender.

"I protest a thousand and one times," replied the governor, "against this threat to a dependency of the Republic without your government's consent."

"Your thousand and one protestations are futile," Toussaint wrote back with grim humor. "It is my intention to occupy the territory purely and simply in the name of the Republic. I will hold you responsible one thousand and one times for any untoward incident that may result from your intransigeance."

And he marched. His foot soldiers traveled with fantastic speed, crossing the mountainous country between Haiti and Santo Domingo City at the rate of forty miles a day. So fast did they go that they finally had to stop and wait for the cavalry to catch up.

This was a bloodless war. The commander-in-chief of the Spanish forces was giving a ball to celebrate his daughter's wedding when the announcement came that

Toussaint was approaching with his black hordes. The handsome Spanish gentlemen kissed their ladies farewell, leaped on their horses and dashed gallantly off to battle. After one brush with Toussaint's businesslike veterans, the brave Spaniards fled in every direction. Toussaint entered Santo Domingo City without a fight. The governor was hostile at first. However, he was quickly won over by Toussaint's dignified friendliness, his modesty and his polished ease. The old slave was no rough diamond. He had become an astute diplomat. He knew how to make himself friendly with the proudest nobleman, the wiliest politician, the humblest field worker or the most savage black general. Still he could retain his aloof superiority.

But he was insulted once during the banquet that followed the peaceful surrender. He asked the mayor of the city about the ruin which stood on the bank of the river.

"It is the palace of Christopher Columbus," answered the mayor. "He was sent to Spain in chains for wishing to make himself independent."

Toussaint answered this gibe coolly. "I know as well as you," he said, "that Columbus was rewarded with ingratitude by Spain. Such is the lot of most men who serve their country. They have powerful enemies who sooner or later manage to undermine them. No doubt the same fate is reserved for me."

Toussaint had clearly prophesied his own end.

Taking a tour of his new domain, Toussaint found the Spanish inhabitants living in the utmost squalor. Their shabby huts were surrounded by thousands of acres of fertile land covered with cattle. Yet they had no milk. When they were hungry, they would slaughter a beef, skin it, cut the flesh into long, thin pieces and hang it on poles to dry in the sun. They lived on this until it was gone. Then they slaughtered another. They grew no vegetables nor fruit. Most families had a tiny plot, but all they raised was tobacco for the cigars which they smoked incessantly. Their furniture usually consisted of one hammock, and their clothes were rags.

Toussaint set to work to bring this half-dead country to life. The Spanish colonists were inefficient and lazy, but they were very proud. Toussaint moved gently, knowing they would not readily accept a black slave as their ruler. He improved roads and built a great new highway. He started schools. He encouraged agriculture by making taxes low and inviting planters from abroad to come and get land on easy terms. He wiped out the bands of marauders who had terrorized the land for years.

Now Haiti was protected along its border by a peaceful, friendly, busy San Domingo.

Toussaint prepared his final and decisive act of defiance. He wrote a constitution for his country.

"I have taken my flight in the realm of eagles," he said. "I must be prudent in alighting on the earth. I can be placed only on a rock, and that rock must be a constitutional government."

If Toussaint had accomplished nothing else, this Constitution would stand as a monument to his extraordinary genius as a statesman. It was not a completely democratic one like ours. He knew that his people were not yet ready to be given the vote. But it insured freedom and equal rights and justice to everyone, which is the basis of democracy. It named Toussaint governor for five years, with the authority to prolong his own term, or to choose his successor.

The most interesting part of the Constitution—and the part that was to make Napoleon angriest—was its definition of Haiti's relation to France. Toussaint was

Defiantly Toussaint wrote a constitution for Haiti

working toward an independent Haiti, but he did not want to break entirely with France. He knew that his backward country needed France's protection, her guidance, her advice. But he wanted Haiti to have absolute local independence. Therefore his Constitution said that there should be French representatives to advise and educate his country, but that they should not be allowed to interfere in any way with Haiti's government. France was to be a big brother.

This idea of local independence was, in fact, more than half a century ahead of its time. The uneducated slave, working alone with no precedent to guide him, had developed the modern idea of "dominion status." This means that a colony governs itself but depends on the mother country for advice in a few matters of importance. The idea was to become the basis of the British Empire, starting with Canada in 1867. But in Toussaint's day it was unheard of and unthought of.

The Constitution also gave Haiti freedom to trade with any country in the world. No one had ever considered letting colonies trade with anyone they pleased. Before this they had traded only with the mother country, to that country's great advantage. The idea of free trade was shocking.

Toussaint's Constitution produced consternation on all sides. Napoleon was outraged even though Toussaint sent him the Constitution for ratification. Toussaint's closest advisers looked on the Constitution as nothing but a dangerous trick to assert Haiti's independence. His generals were opposed to it, and they began to mutter and threaten. Two of the most popular generals, Christophe and Moïse, even went so far as to talk openly of revolt.

"The Constitution is a crime," said Christophe. "It is foolish to imagine that we can govern ourselves. We should be grateful if they allow us to occupy a few offices. I will revolt against Toussaint rather than support his pretensions."

Moïse was even more bitter. "What does the old fool want?" he asked. "He thinks he is King of Haiti. Against whom is he arming? Where will he get his soldiers? For it won't be we, General, who will lead our men against the French. We shall see what we shall see!"

These short-sighted black leaders did not realize that their country was already independent before Toussaint wrote his Constitution. They did not realize that the wise old man had worked out the only possible fair relation to France. Far worse, they did not realize that Napoleon was secretly preparing an all-out attack on their country before the Constitution was even thought of. His aim was to reduce it again to a helpless dependency and to restore slavery. At the time Toussaint most needed solidarity in his country, his generals were getting ready to betray him.

But he bravely proclaimed his Constitution. At three o'clock in the morning of July 7, 1801, before the heat of the day, the bells tolled and the drums rolled in the city of Cap François. The garrison marched to the Place d'Armes in the center of the city. Thousands of people were massed there. Every house had a flag. The Altar of the Fatherland, a temple which had been erected to commemorate Sonthonax's emancipation decree, was decorated with bunting and palms. At five o'clock there came a colorful procession of civil, military and church authorities. Toussaint wore a general's dress uniform. He looked grave and solemn. He knew this was the final act of defiance, and that his country's greatest struggle lay just ahead.

He was greeted with a tremendous roar of cheering: "Papa Toussaint! Papa Toussaint!"

He spoke simply, telling his people what was in the

Constitution, and what were to be the duties of each class of citizens. After the ceremony there was a Te Deum in the church, then a great banquet at the Government Palace. Merrymaking went on all day and all night, and the entire city was lighted up. Heralds were sent all over the land to proclaim the Constitution, and all prisoners were turned free except those guilty of the most serious crimes.

Papa Toussaint stood at the very top. But on this lonely peak he had no friends. His generals were angry with him. General Moïse, his own nephew, revolted openly and was promptly executed. General Christophe, who was later to make himself King of Haiti, was secretly trying to devise a way to overthrow Toussaint. General Dessalines, always violent, was calling for an immediate break with France and telling the people Toussaint was too cautious. The white planters, hearing rumors of the French army which was soon to come, began chafing at taxes, threatening their black workers and openly defying Toussaint's regime. His own black people could not understand this "dominion status." They did not see why Toussaint should not break completely with France. For the first time, they were not solidly behind him.

As Toussaint announced the Constitution, Napoleon was writing secret instructions for the reconquest of Haiti.

8

"Races Melt Beneath His Hand"

SO FAR THIS HAS BEEN ONLY A STORY OF WAR. IN HIS ten years of leadership Toussaint had a little over two years, between 1799 and 1801, without war. But ordinary daily life goes on even while soldiers are fighting. In Haiti it not only went on, but it got better and better. Haiti was changed in these ten years from a burned, ravaged, divided land full of hatred and savagery to a peaceful, happy, highly organized little country.

Toussaint's first problem was to get his country back on its feet economically. He had to do this with thoroughness, and he had to do it in a hurry. So he instituted military rule on the plantations. The field hands were regarded as soldiers, who are not allowed to leave their battalions without permission. The foremen and plantation owners were the officers, who were to see that discipline was maintained. A general of the army

121

was put in charge of each district. There was a fair system of distribution of profits so that the workers got one-quarter of the produce. No whipping and no coercion were allowed. But they had to work. A worker couldn't do the easiest, laziest thing which was to go off and cultivate his own little plot. The big estates had to be kept together for the country to produce efficiently. If the white owners didn't come back, the estates were turned over to the government and run by the higher officers of the army. A great many of the owners did come back, to help willingly in putting their country on its feet again. Because, under Toussaint's rule, it *was* their country, as well as the blacks' country, and for the first time they began to take pride in it.

Toussaint had a simple, universal tax system that everyone could understand. He got rid of all the clumsy, complicated taxes of the old regime. He also got rid of the corrupt tax officials who stole from both the people and the government. Everyone had to pay the same fixed percentage; everyone knew what he had to pay; and the system was strictly supervised. There was no room for corruption. He instituted courts all over the country, and for the first time there was equal justice in Haiti. Everywhere there were schools, though in the old Haiti there had been none for blacks or whites. The soldiers of the army had to attend both morning and evening church services, and the African religion was sternly forbidden. Toussaint himself was a highly moral man, in an age when there was great corruption. His strict rules were like a breath of clean air.

By the time Toussaint published his Constitution in 1801, Haiti was back to two-thirds of its pre-Revolutionary production. Its people were proud, prosperous and happy. No longer did a Negro have to be ashamed of being black. No longer did a white man have to fear the vengeance of his oppressed workers. No longer did a mulatto have to live in a twilight of injustice and contempt. There was complete equality of color. Blacks, whites and mulattoes mixed freely without scorn or fear.

Many of the Negroes became very grand. Although some had had only the barest coverings of rags, they now went to the opposite extreme and dressed in elaborate finery. Their houses were sumptuously furnished. They developed an extreme etiquette and politeness which put many Europeans to shame. Their natural wit and gaiety now had full play, and the streets and houses rang with their high laughter. There were several theaters with all black players who had a remarkable talent for acting. One heard music everywhere; there was always dancing at night.

At Le Cap there was a hotel, la République, which was as fine as any in Europe. It had a magnificent foyer which was always crowded—black military men in full regalia, elegant mulattoes with long-tailed satin coats and ruffled shirts, white planters in white suits and broad straw hats. Its dining room had long tables piled high with Haiti's richest dishes. Here a general might sit next to a drummer, who would help himself freely from his superior's dishes. A coal-black colonel would explain military tactics to an American merchant, illustrating with a pencil on the tablecloth.

A stranger might wonder who was the inconspicuous little black man in the wrinkled white linen suit who was smiling affably and somewhat shyly at the coarse jokes of the soldiers around him. No one seemed in the least awe of him, and the stranger would be immensely surprised and almost shocked to learn that this was Toussaint Louverture.

What kind of man was the ruler of this happy land? Toussaint could be very grand and proud, too, when he appeared at a military review on Bel-Argent. He would be surrounded by his bodyguard of fifteen hundred of the handsomest, most courageous and most loyal of his soldiers in elegant sky-blue uniforms. This was a different person from the mild, relaxed little man at the Hotel de la République. At these reviews Toussaint appeared in full-dress uniform: a tight blue jacket, a large red cape flung over his shoulder, red cuffs with eight rows of gold lace on his arms, an enormous pair of gold epaulets on his shoulders, scarlet waistcoat, white pantaloons and shining black boots. On his head was a round hat with a red feather sticking straight up, and at his side a huge sword.

He gave the people a fine show as he and his company, followed by a noisy German regimental band, marched to the plain outside Le Cap to review and exercise thousands of troops. When Toussaint appeared the massed ranks of soldiers snapped to attention with perfect precision. At a whistle a whole brigade ran three or four hundred yards, the men separated, then threw themselves flat on the ground, changing to the backs and sides and keeping up a strong, continuous fire. At another whistle they re-formed ranks with incredible speed and perfection. This was the tactic Toussaint had

developed for combatting cavalry in bush or hilly country. Europeans, watching, marveled, not so much at the
beautifully oiled machine of Toussaint's army, as at the
high morale and evident good spirit of the soldiers.
They needed no coercion; they loved their leader.

A still different Toussaint appeared in the evening in
the big reception room at the Government Palace at Le
Cap. He had remodeled the Palace. The walls and floors
were of white marble with white marble columns. The
furnishings were in the gold and damask baroque style
of Louis XVI. The old slave liked French eighteenth
century elegance, and he had natural good taste. Anyone could come to his "circles," which were held every
evening. Toussaint would circulate among the guests,
joking with soldiers, listening to complaints of laborers,
discussing crops with planters. Amid the colorful finery
of his guests the black leader stood out for his simplic-
ity. Again he wore the planter's garb—a white suit and a
broad-brimmed straw hat.

"Dominus tecum, salve Domino, tibi gratias!" he
would cry, coming up to a group of Negro officers. They
would look at him with puzzled awe. He would say
gravely, "You don't know Latin? Too bad! You will
never get very far." Then he would burst out laughing.

A black laborer would approach him shyly and stammer that he would no longer work for his white employer because he just didn't like whites. Toussaint would pick up a glass of wine and a glass of water, mix them together and say, "How can you tell which is which? We must all live together."

After a while he would retire to an inner room, taking a few friends with him, usually white planters. They would talk for an hour or so. When they left, Toussaint called in his five secretaries and started dictating. He dictated hundreds of letters a day, to say nothing of military reports, proclamations and speeches. He would dictate half of an important letter to one secretary. Then he would suddenly send the secretary on an errand and finish up the letter with another secretary. No one must know too much about what he was doing. He would dictate far into the night. Usually he slept only about two hours. He ate no meat and drank no wine. Sometimes he went for days eating nothing but a few bananas.

His activity was prodigious, and he seemed tireless. He habitually covered about one hundred twenty-five miles a day. He would change horses frequently—for he had hundreds of thoroughbred horses stabled all over the country—and outdistance his guards, who were not able to keep up with him. No one knew where he was going, what he was doing, when he was coming back, where he had been. He would turn up unexpectedly at a plantation, inspect it, then gallop off to a town to give out prizes at a school. A few hours later he would appear at a fort, see that it was manned properly and that the artillery was in order. There he would be provided with a coach and leave in style. A few miles away he would get out of the coach, mount a horse and ride off in the opposite direction.

When he came to a small village, he would dismount and go into one of the shabbiest houses. He knew people everywhere. An old woman would prepare him *callaloos*, a kind of vegetable broth, and he would chat with her while he drank it. He was simple and kindly with his own people, but he could appear stern, despotic or sly with those he distrusted.

A white émigré planter came to him with a curt demand that he be given a larger share of the produce of his plantation. Toussaint refused to consider the request. The planter argued and tried to threaten Toussaint, saying that he had influence with Napoleon Bonaparte. Toussaint looked at him with an impenetrable stare. Then he said:

"Bonaparte is very cunning, the French government has always been very cunning, and you too, sir, are pretty cunning. But neither you nor the French government nor Bonaparte with all his generals shall ever be able to find out what is in this head, nor ever discover what I have resolved—no, never!"

Mysterious, tireless, stern and gentle by turns, elegantly polished with whites, simple and homely with his own people—Toussaint was a leader whom no one could resist and no one could understand. He was a dictator. In these days we have learned to distrust dictators; the word suggests despotism and oppression. But Toussaint never abused his power. With him country came first. He only did what was best for Haiti; of his own fate he thought nothing. He did not want personal power. He wanted a strong, proud, independent Haiti. It has been well said of Toussaint that he was more than just a man —he was a nation.

His natural kindness kept him from being cruel and oppressive as most dictators become after a while. Toussaint was a truly good man. For this, much more than for his military prowess and his diplomatic polish, his people loved him and would do whatever he said.

Toussaint was happiest and most natural when he was

As he drank his broth, he chatted with the old woman (p. 128)

at home on his own plantation. His good-natured Suzan
had grown tremendously fat. She was a happy, un-
affected woman, and she provided a restful haven for
Toussaint. At home he would ride around the plantation
watching the field workers, discussing problems with
his manager. He knew all his workers and interested
himself in everything that went on in their families. In
the evenings he and Suzan would watch them dance the
chica. Sometimes they joined in, to the immense delight of the people. Toussaint was interested in precious

and semiprecious stones, and had a beautiful collection. He also collected weapons of all kinds. In his room there were always flowers, and in his house there was always music. He had adopted a little orphan girl who had run after him in a village street and called him "Papa." He loved children. His own two half-grown sons were in school in Paris, hostages of the French government, and he missed them.

So, in the midst of war, Haiti had peace. While Napoleon was hatching his cunning schemes in Paris, Toussaint in Haiti was strengthening his people through love, pride and unity.

9

The Master Plotter

THERE WAS NO LONGER A REVOLUTION IN FRANCE. Napoleon now sat where the deputies had so enthusiastically proclaimed the freedom of the slaves. He was like a small deadly spider, spinning webs over the whole of the western world. He called the seaport merchants to him and asked them about Haiti. Since a large part of their wealth came from the slave trade, the merchants had been angry ever since the emancipation decree.

"Slavery is the only profitable way to run the colonies," they told Napoleon.

"Then by all means let us restore slavery," said Napoleon.

Once he had uttered this fateful sentence, Napoleon began to think of a thousand good reasons to invade the colony. Haiti was the center of the French colonial system, he told himself. Now it belonged in name only to France. It really belonged to the blacks, who might free themselves at any moment from the mother country and cut off a large part of French wealth at its source. Toussaint was nothing but a "gilded African," who was aping him, Napoleon thought. Why, he even let himself be called "Bonaparte of the Antilles," although his empire consisted of only a few hundred thousand ragged ex-slaves. Napoleon let himself get very angry about this imitative black upstart.

In France itself there were good reasons for the expedition. A large part of the army which had brought Napoleon to power was strongly republican. The soldiers still believed in the Revolution. Now Napoleon was already considering the idea of making himself Emperor, and he knew there might be trouble with these democratic men. He was afraid of his own soldiers.

"There are sixty thousand men," he said to one of his closest friends, "whom I would like to send as far away from France as possible."

But Napoleon didn't really need reasons. He gave the truest of all when he said, "I am for the whites because I am white. I have no other reason. That one is enough."

He worked himself up to a pitch of indignation about his unmanageable little colony. Then he began to look further, beyond the reconquest of Haiti, to a magnificent dream. Haiti at this time traded chiefly with the United States, which was the closest country and the friendliest. This irked Napoleon and the merchants who backed him. He would like Haiti to trade exclusively with France and its colonies. There was the Louisiana Territory for example. It was a huge, potentially wealthy French colony to the west of the then small and weak United States. The Louisiana Territory could be made the center of commerce with the French colonies in the Caribbean Sea. This would cut out the United States entirely.

Napoleon gave far-reaching orders about his North American colony. Both banks of the Mississippi were to be fortified as far up as civilization had penetrated. Adventurers in the American West were to be bribed or frightened over to the side of the French. Every Indian tribe within reach was to be bought. Louisiana was to be an armed fortress. Napoleon figured it would take about two months to reconquer Haiti. When that was done, he would send his army of sixty thousand men on to Louisiana. The little United States would have on its western boundary one of the most threatening armies in the world. Napoleon's dreams of empire were endless.

What was to prevent him from moving his soldiers into the United States?

Our country was ready to be picked like a ripe apple. We had at that time only a tiny army and almost no navy —exactly seven frigates of war! Just twenty years before we had finished freeing ourselves from another oppressive power, and we were much too busy building up our new democracy to keep a large, expensive standing army. President Jefferson knew that the life of our new democracy would be snuffed out like a candle if he could not keep peace. He didn't know, of course, exactly what Napoleon had up his sleeve. But he watched with alarm the building of fortresses along the Mississippi. Our little country was weak and divided, and it was dangerously threatened from outside. We were in a very tight spot.

Napoleon prepared his expeditionary force. He put many of his best generals in charge of it and headed it with Leclerc, his own brother-in-law. To Leclerc he gave secret instructions. Haiti was to be pacified in exactly two months on a definite schedule. First Leclerc was to deceive the Haitians and win their confidence by telling

them that their freedom would be respected. Gradually
he would take away the power of the blacks, arrest Toussaint and the other leaders, disband the army, take
away the muskets from the people and, at the end, restore slavery. Then Leclerc was to take his army and go
to Louisiana, which was ready to receive him. It was all
down in black and white. Napoleon was very sure of himself. He even added a contemptuous footnote on the
United States:

"The only nation toward whom you may be obliged
to assume a hostile attitude is the United States, which
may be seized with a fit of madness. Two warships and a
few frigates will suffice to keep them in check." He
didn't think much of our power, and unfortunately he
was right! We did what we could to help Toussaint, however, short of actually going to war. We supplied thirty
thousand muskets and plenty of ammunition and food.
Toussaint paid for everything he got from us.

Before Napoleon started on his great Western adventure, he made sure that in Europe he was safe. England
was the only country with whom he was still at war. He
quickly made peace with her. Then he told the English
that he was going to depose the Haitian chief in order to
keep slave rebellions from starting all over the Carib-

bean. England owned several rich islands in this area. Though the British were afraid of Napoleon they were still more afraid of revolution in their colonies. The American Revolution had taught the British a disastrous lesson. So they agreed to help the French leader.

Napoleon fooled his own soldiers as well as everyone else in the vast network of lies he had built up. He told them they were fighting for the French Republic against a black traitor who had sold himself to priests, émigré French royalists and England. With the expedition he sent the mulatto generals who had run away to France after the civil war. To these men he promised control of the island once Toussaint was deposed. To Leclerc he said secretly:

"Get rid of the mulatto generals as soon as you find they are of no further use to you. Put them on a ship and send them to Madagascar."

There were some dissenting voices in France. Vincent, Toussaint's trusted white general, had come to France to present Toussaint's Constitution to Napoleon. The expeditionary force was all ready to sail when he arrived, but the Constitution sent Napoleon into a towering rage.

"I will teach this black upstart a lesson!" he shouted. "A slave cannot defy Napoleon."

"Sire, leave Haiti alone!" pleaded Vincent. "It is the happiest spot in your dominions. God meant this man to govern. Races melt beneath his hand. He has saved you this island."

Napoleon replied by banishing Vincent to the island of Elba.

Many of the white planters who lived in France were equally leery of the expedition. They knew the power Toussaint had over his people and the strength of the freedom-loving black army. The French generals, they said, didn't know what they were up against. Leclerc, the leader of the expedition, said scornfully to one of his captains, who had been a planter:

"All these blacks, when they see an army, will lay down their arms. They will be only too happy that we pardon them."

"You have been misinformed, General," said the captain.

"But there is a colonist who told me he is ready to go into the interior of the country and arrest Toussaint with sixty grenadiers."

"I know there are coxcombs everywhere," answered

To Toussaint the French fleet looked hopelessly strong (p. 140)

the captain. "He has more hardihood than I. I should
not care to undertake it with less than sixty thousand."

The captain was promptly dismissed from the expedition.

The first quota of troops set sail in January, 1802. It
was to be the largest expeditionary force ever sent over-
seas. It contained forty thousand men and forty generals, and included eighty-six war vessels. It was
supplied with everything from cannon to nails. As pas-
sengers it carried Toussaint's two sons. They were be-

ing sent home to help innocently in deceiving the black leader in the first phase. The boys had been wined and dined by Napoleon before they sailed. Each had been presented with a magnificent military costume including full armor.

The expedition also contained Pauline, Napoleon's sister and the wife of Leclerc. She was a beautiful, languid lady used to the frivolities of the French court. She brought with her a large retinue of actors, musicians and dandified courtiers, who were to entertain her in her barbaric new home. At the last minute Pauline got scared and had to be carried forcibly on board.

Less than half the expedition reached Haiti, the rest being driven to other ports by storms. The part that did arrive at the harbor of Le Cap looked hopelessly strong to Toussaint who stood on a mountain above the city.

"We shall perish!" he cried. "All France is come to overwhelm us." It was his only moment of panic. But he pulled himself together immediately. He jumped on his horse and galloped down to the city to give instructions to General Christophe not to allow the French to land.

Now Christophe, as we have seen before, had no wish to fight the French. He was afraid, and he was prepared

to surrender Le Cap without a fight. Then his leader
came dashing in. Christophe was still more in awe of
Toussaint than he was of the French. Toussaint told him
what to say to the French envoy, and told him to say it
loud. He, Toussaint, would be hiding in a nearby room
to hear that his orders were carried out.

Christophe put on a smooth show. "I am awaiting the
governor's orders," he said to the envoy from the
French fleet. He spoke politely, but his voice did not
waver. "Until I hear from him I cannot permit you to
land. If you use force I will resist, and if you succeed
in making a landing, you will enter a city reduced to
ashes. Even on those ashes I will continue to combat
you. You are building a house of cards that will be scattered by the wind."

All that day Toussaint's soldiers went from door to
door in Le Cap telling the people to leave the city. A
steady stream of people made their way up to the hills
back of the city, taking with them everything they could
carry. Negro women carried enormous bundles on their
heads; ladies rode in carriages piled high with boxes;
children pushed heavy carts; donkeys struggled up the
steep trails with loads larger than they were. The people
often turned and looked back at their city. It seemed

enchanted as the setting sun touched its pink, white and yellow houses. When night fell, the people were still streaming out of the city.

Suddenly they heard the cannon of the fort boom. The French were landing! In a moment the whole city was alight as black soldiers ran from house to house with their torches. General Christophe himself was one of the first to start the flames. He went through his luxurious house methodically firing each room.

The people on the hills turned to watch in fascinated horror as their lovely city went up in flames. As they watched, there was an enormous explosion that lit up the sky for miles and set huge rocks rolling down the hill on the helpless fugitives. The powder magazine had been fired.

Next morning the French troops marched into a shell of a city. Out of two thousand houses, only fifty-nine remained. The once-white pavements were black and sticky with burned sugar that had flowed from the warehouses. The delicate iron balcony railings were twisted. The pink, blue and yellow walls were blackened and crumbling. And through gaping holes one could see charred bits of furniture and broken beams.

Pauline Leclerc looked with dismay on the hideous

General Christophe set fire to his own house

ruin of the fabulous city where she had hoped to reign like a queen. French troops in their neat white uniforms and shining black boots marched with precision through the ruined streets. But into their minds crept the first frightening hint of the disaster that awaited them in this country.

10

"Their Bones Will Be Scattered Among the Mountains"

THE TIME LIMITS THAT NAPOLEON HAD SET CAME AND went. The blacks showed no signs of being subdued. In the beginning it looked easy for the French. They took over the main cities and the coastal plains without difficulty. This was the fault of Toussaint's generals, who defied the wise old leader.

Toussaint had devised a strategy which would have made short work of the French. He wanted to keep most of his army in the mountains, leaving a few soldiers in each port city. Wherever the French landed this garrison was to set fire to the city and then fall back, burning the plantations on the way. Then Toussaint could jump on each French landing party with his big, fast-moving army, and destroy it.

But Christophe and the others thought that Toussaint was being cautious and cowardly. "We have arms," they said. "Let us use them." Toussaint's control over his fierce and independent generals was weakening. To preserve the unity of the army he had to give in. He was forced to scatter his army all over the country. So wherever the French landed, they found a much smaller force of blacks whom they defeated easily.

Many blacks deserted Toussaint's army and went over to the French. They believed Napoleon's false promises. And they were frightened when they saw the high-stepping French cavalry and the formidable artillery, followed by the endless lines of well-groomed French

Invisible blacks shot at them from all directions (p. 148)

soldiers. In a short time the French held most of the important points. Toussaint's army was growing smaller and smaller.

But still Leclerc could not carry out Napoleon's orders. If the blacks were beaten, they refused to show it. Leclerc could not arrest the black leaders; he could not disarm the populace. He could not get anywhere near Toussaint, who was as elusive as a will-o'-the-wisp. He seemed to be everywhere and nowhere. The French would come into a town and find it burned to the ground. The wells would be stopped up with dead horses. The roads would be torn up. The plantations around the town would be smoking and deserted. The French would take possession. But as soon as they moved on, the blacks would come in from nowhere and take the town back again. The French would find a road blocked with fallen trees and huge rocks, or they would fall into deep ditches hidden with thorny bushes. As they struggled to get rid of these obstacles they would be shot down by blacks hidden in the tops of coconut trees. When they marched through a narrow mountain pass, rocks would fall on them from the steep slopes; and invisible blacks would shoot at them from every direction.

For three months Leclerc and his army struggled against this elusive and impossible enemy. French supplies began to run low. American merchants in Le Cap and the other cities had plenty of supplies. But Leclerc insulted them, called them "Arabs," threw them in jail and when they refused to sell to him he tried to steal what he could not buy. The Americans would have nothing to do with him.

Leclerc's soldiers began sickening in the moist, unhealthy climate. They did not have enough to eat; they could not stand the heat; they had not the proper clothes; they didn't even have shoes. Everywhere one saw French soldiers begging in the streets. Under Toussaint's rule there had been no beggars.

The French officers, on the other hand, were corrupt and greedy. While the French soldiers starved, sickened and died in the hills, their superiors caroused in the towns in an atmosphere of feverish gaiety. Le Cap had not yet been rebuilt. It was a city of tents and ruined palaces and shelters made with a few boards laid over the broken walls. There French officers gambled and drank and courted the Creole ladies. Wooden huts along the main streets offered new fashions and expensive trinkets from Paris. There was no public entertainment, and the only amusement was scandal. The burned houses contained quantities of valuables which their owners had not been able to carry away before the fire. French officers stole whatever took their fancy. They also accepted bribes from the inhabitants for the smallest favors. The result was that many of them became extremely rich. One young lieutenant came from France a poor man. When he died a few months later, he was a general and owned thirty thousand dollars and a

Pauline called in a mulatto general to amuse her

large quantity of silver plate. Leclerc himself used army money to have a set of solid silver plate made for Pauline. In the meantime, Pauline sat in a darkened room, bored and languid. She complained that there were no parties, and called in one of the mulatto generals to amuse her while she received the Creole ladies of Le Cap.

There was a fortress in a steep mountain pass overlooking one of the largest and most fertile of Haiti's coastal plains. This fortress, called Crête-à-Pierrot, barred the way into the interior of Haiti. Leclerc knew he had to take Crête-à-Pierrot in order to get at Toussaint and his highly dangerous little army.

Toussaint knew this too. He also knew that the fortress could be made almost impregnable, and that a mere handful of men could defend it against a large army. He knew that if he could force Leclerc to waste men and time taking Crête-à-Pierrot, it would be worth a hundred victories in the field. Toussaint needed only time. In a few weeks the rainy season would start, and then the French soldiers would die like flies of yellow fever. Natives of the West Indies were immune to it, but it was a dreaded scourge for Europeans. Once yellow fever hit them, the French could easily be pushed out of Haiti.

So Toussaint sent the savage Dessalines up to Crête-à-Pierrot with orders to strengthen it and defend it at any cost. Toussaint knew that for foolhardy bravery he could always depend on Dessalines, who loved a fight better than he loved life, and had no fear.

While Dessalines strengthened Crête-à-Pierrot, Toussaint and his guerrilla army kept picking away at the French. Toussaint had munitions and food stored all over the mountains in secret hiding places. He and his men would dash down to the plain and destroy one of Leclerc's outposts, or ambush some unfortunate French troops who got too far from home. Then they would climb again to the nearest camp before the French knew what had hit them. The blacks knew invisible trails through the tangled mountains. They could make their way up the steepest precipices, could wade through foul-smelling swamps and find their way through dense jungle choked with vines. Living close to the earth, they loved and knew the mountains as well as their own backyards. The French couldn't possibly catch them. They were courageous and unbeatable, and they laughed at death. Liberty and the possession of their own beloved country were more important to them than life. They had no doubts now about whom they were fighting—it was Napoleon, who wanted to enslave them again. Toussaint continually spurred them on with his eloquent words:

"You are fighting against enemies who have neither faith, law nor religion. They promise you liberty but they intend your servitude. If you are not their slaves they call you rebels. Uncover your breasts, you will see them branded by the iron of slavery. During ten years what have you not undertaken for liberty? Your oppressors are slain or put to flight; the English humiliated by defeat; discord extinguished; a land of slavery purified by fire and reviving more beautiful than ever under liberty.

"Now you are carrying everywhere consuming fires, the torches of your liberty. The steps of our enemies have trodden only on ashes, their eyes have encountered nothing but smoking ruins, which you have watered with their blood. Not for *their* country, not for *their* liberty are they fighting, but only to serve the hatred and ambition of Bonaparte, my enemy—mine because he is yours! This sky, these mountains, these lakes, all are strange to them. As soon as they breathe the same air as we, their bravery sinks, their courage departs. Those whom the sword spares will be struck down by an avenging climate. Their bones will be scattered among these mountains and rocks and tossed about by the waves of our sea. Nevermore will they behold their native land, and liberty will reign over their tombs!"

But Leclerc still had many more men than Toussaint, and was gradually drawing a steel ring around the diminished black army. Now was the time when Leclerc must attack Crête-à-Pierrot, get through to the interior and smash the black army once for all. He didn't propose to do this by halves. He sent twelve thousand men and four of his best generals with orders to stop at nothing. Leclerc had learned by this time that he wasn't fighting frightened, half-wild slaves, but a disciplined, spirited, fantastically courageous army. He wasn't cocksure any more. He was getting desperate.

Dessalines had ordered his men to rebuild the crumbling walls of the old fort. Outside it, on the steep slope of the ravine, he had told them to clear away every bush, every tree, every blade of grass. Then they dug many little ditches, each a foot deep, all the way down the slope. When they had fulfilled this mysterious order, about half of the men stayed outside the fort. They built fires, they laughed and sang, they rattled kettles. Some of them lay down as if sleeping. They didn't look like an army; they looked like gypsies.

Inside the fort Dessalines paced about ferociously. He was naked to the waist, and there was a hole in his hat where a bullet had gone through. He talked angrily to his men, telling them what they would do to the French. He strode about the ramparts watching for the French troops. Finally they appeared. Dessalines picked up a torch and approached a barrel of powder.

"We are going to be attacked," he shouted. "If the French put their feet in here, I shall blow everything up!" The men cheered.

Outside, the black soldiers seemed to be oblivious of the approaching enemy. Their high laughter rang down the ravine, and they appeared to be entirely at ease.

The French approached, marching with precision, as on parade. Their boots gleamed, and their white uniforms were spotless. When the black soldiers outside the fort saw them, they dropped their kettles and muskets and started shrieking and running around helplessly, as if frightened out of their wits.

Suddenly a cannon boomed. Dessalines had given the order. As if by magic all the black soldiers in the ravine disappeared. They had jumped into those little ditches. The guns and cannons of the fort opened up, and the neat white lines of the French were mowed down. The ones coming up from behind were in complete confusion, and the black soldiers leaped out of their ditches and jumped on them with knives and pistols.

The French suffered terrible losses that day, and Crête-à-Pierrot was still intact. Reinforcements were sent up, and the French tried it again. The same neatly spaced columns climbed the hill; the same blacks were outside the fort, playing and singing; the same signal sounded, and the same slaughter took place. Believe it or not, the French tried it a third time with exactly the same results! By now the four generals were wounded, and the French had lost a large number of men. They decided to wait it out. Eventually Crête-à-Pierrot would have to give up through lack of food.

Inside the fort there were only twelve hundred men. The spirit was high although they were surrounded by a French army of nearly twelve thousand. When the water ran low, the blacks kept balls of lead in their mouths to quench their thirst. Officers asked for doses of poison to keep from being captured alive. The wounded begged to be killed by their companions in case the fort was evacuated. Red flags were run up on the four corners of the fortress to show that they would not surrender and would show no mercy. No one complained. The soldiers sang revolutionary songs and shouted taunts to the French outside.

The unhappy French soldiers, camping on the unfriendly mountainside, heard the songs. And they wondered, as they had wondered often during the last months, why they were fighting. Napoleon had told them they were fighting for the Revolution against traitors. But surely these black soldiers, with the songs of the Revolution on their lips and the deathless courage of liberty in their hearts, were not traitors.

One morning a black soldier appeared in the French camp. He said he was a deserter from Toussaint's army. A French general came to question him. The black seemed overcome by fear. He stammered and trembled. All the time his eyes kept roving wildly around the French camp. Suddenly he straightened up and made a dash. The French general grabbed at him; the black turned and nearly bit off his thumb. The black ran under the legs of a horse, threw over some soldiers who tried to stop him and jumped in the river amid a hail of bullets. At the other side he limped away, wounded, but some of his comrades ran out of the woods to help him. This man was a spy, and he had found out what he wanted to know, which was the approximate size and strength of the French besieging force. His information was carried back to Toussaint. Realizing that Crête-à-Pierrot could not hold out much longer, Toussaint sent orders for it to be evacuated.

The next morning a blind old man and a deaf old woman hobbled into the French camp. They could neither talk sensibly nor understand anything. The French soldiers shouted at them and beat them, but they only huddled together and piteously begged to be allowed to go home. The French finally let them go. Once beyond the range of French fire the two old wrecks suddenly started leaping about, thumbing their noses at the French soldiers and jeering at them. Then they ran nimbly up the hill toward the fortress. These were the messengers bringing Toussaint's order to evacuate.

In the middle of the night Dessalines and his fearless soldiers crept out of the fortress. They made a dash through the surrounding French lines. The French were taken so completely by surprise that they couldn't even find their guns. Their general, the proud Rochambeau, ran away in his night clothes. By the time the French

In the middle of the night they crept out of the fortress

had pulled themselves together, the blacks had vanished. In the fortress nothing was left. The guns were ruined, all the food and ammunition destroyed.

The French had Crête-à-Pierrot, but it had cost them thousands of men and far too much time. It was more of a defeat than a victory. Leclerc was so ashamed that he wouldn't tell Napoleon about it. Instead he kept writing letters telling how much land the French soldiers had conquered. At the end of each letter he begged desperately for more food and arms and money. It was easy for Napoleon to understand what was really going on in Haiti, and he didn't like it. Like most greedy, vain and faithless people, he began to look in other directions for easier territories to conquer. His interest in Haiti grew fitful, and he closed his eyes to the disaster that was going on there. Without reinforcements Leclerc had no hope of going on from Crête-à-Pierrot and finishing off Toussaint. The black leader was clearly on the way to victory. This was in spite of the fact that he had lost half his forces through desertion. And yellow fever was not winning the war. Long before the rains and the yellow fever season Leclerc had lost 10,000 French soldiers, half of them killed, the other half sick or wounded. And he had not even completed his first instructions. He battled hopelessly with a courageous and elusive enemy while his supplies ran lower and lower and Napoleon looked the other way. In a few weeks the French army would have been finished.

But suddenly a heartbreaking thing happened to Toussaint and gave new life to the French. General Christophe deserted him and went over to the side of the French, taking with him a large part of the black army.

Christophe had been angry at Toussaint ever since the Constitution had been published. He possessed neither Toussaint's wisdom nor his caution. He did not understand that the old black leader knew to the exact moment when it was wise to defy and when to compromise. He saw only that the black army was getting smaller, and he wanted to surrender before everything was lost. He did not understand Toussaint's strategy of striking short blows at the French, while waiting for the French army to fall to pieces under the ravages of yellow fever and starvation.

He gave no reason for his betrayal, beyond saying petulantly that he was tired of living like a savage. Christophe was patriotic, but he was stupid.

The betrayal was a fearful blow to Toussaint. But the

indomitable old leader did not lose heart. He had two choices now. He had about four thousand men left, not enough to harry the French with any success. He could hole up in the mountains, defy the French and wait for the rainy season. Or he could go boldly to Leclerc, tell him he wanted to make peace, and *then* sit back and wait for the rainy season. By this move his men could go home, could see their families and live like human beings for the first time in many months. But they would hold themselves ready for the signal to rise and push the weakened, sick French troops into the sea.

Toussaint sent a message to Leclerc, who was even readier than he to stop this hopeless war. In May, 1802, less than four months after the French had landed, an armistice was arranged through envoys. Toussaint rode proudly into Le Cap with his dragoons while crowds cheered and girls threw flowers in front of him. Leclerc came out on the square to greet him, embraced him enthusiastically and said, "General, we can only praise you for the way you have borne the burden of governing Haiti. Our reconciliation will make this island blossom anew."

Toussaint drew back coldly from the Frenchman's embrace, frowned and said, "General, I governed a

Leclerc came out on the square to greet Toussaint

peaceful and happy country. For what reason have you brought here sword and fire?" There was no answer to that.

Leclerc invited the black leader to lunch. At the great banquet Toussaint sat silent and stern. He would not touch food, afraid of being poisoned. Toward the end of the meal he had a glass of water and a little bit of cheese, which he cut carefully from near the center. He spoke only once. Leclerc leaned over to him and asked:

"General, if the war had continued, where would you have got supplies?"

Toussaint answered with a hint of a smile, "General, I would have taken them from you." There was no answer to that either.

When he left the conference room after signing the truce, Toussaint found the people waiting for him. Rumors had been flying of a surrender to the French, and the people were weeping and terrified. "Papa Toussaint! Papa Toussaint!" they cried. "Have you deserted us?"

He looked at his people, and his face grew gentle. "No, my children," he said. "All your brothers are under arms, and all our officers will keep their ranks. I will never desert you." The people laughed and cheered again.

The armistice was a clear victory for Toussaint. The blacks of Haiti were still to be free French citizens. There were to be no reprisals. All the Haitian officers were to keep their ranks. Toussaint himself was to keep his staff and retire with honor wherever he wished on the island.

Sick and defeated, Leclerc knew Toussaint had won.

The French might have taken the cities and covered the plains and won over many of the black leaders. But in a few months of war the French army had become a shambles. It was just a matter of time before they would be pushed out. Leclerc had no illusions about the temporary nature of this so-called truce. Toussaint and his uneducated, badly equipped, high-hearted blacks had whipped the best army in Europe.

Toussaint retired to his plantation. He kept his staff near him, and officers came and went at all hours of the day and night. The old leader was not letting go his control. He was following his wise rule of wait and be patient.

But the worst betrayal of all was in store for Toussaint. Moïse had revolted against him and had been shot. Christophe had left him openly in the heat of battle. Now Dessalines, his most trusted general, left him secretly and treacherously. Dessalines had signed the truce when Toussaint did, and had also feigned submission. But Dessalines was a barbarian, without morals or loyalty. Due to his courage and his military genius he had become the most powerful of the generals next to Toussaint. He didn't see why he shouldn't go further and get rid of Toussaint entirely. Then he, Dessalines, could take over the job of pushing out the French, and make himself absolute ruler of Haiti.

To carry out this plan Dessalines first made himself indispensable to the French. He told Leclerc that Toussaint was double-faced and a liar, but that he, Dessalines, was whole-heartedly for the French. To prove this he volunteered to help the French in any mopping-up activities they wanted to do. In a short time he became known as the butcher of the blacks, his own people. While he helped Leclerc, he never stopped urging the arrest of Toussaint. Christophe joined Dessalines in this monstrous deception. He, too, asked for Toussaint's arrest. He, too, helped to murder his fellow countrymen.

Leclerc did not need any urging to arrest Toussaint. It was what he had wanted to do ever since he had landed. How would he do it? The wily old leader would never let himself be arrested. He couldn't be bribed, and he couldn't be tricked. It looked like an impossible assignment.

But Toussaint stood alone, deserted and betrayed. His peaceful, harmonious little country was torn apart. The careful work of ten years was scattered to the winds. The lovely countryside was again ravaged by fire, and the rivers ran with blood. Toussaint's dream of a perfect free state where all would be equal was at an end. He had given his whole soul to his country, and he had defeated the French who wanted to enslave it again. But his own greedy and ambitious generals had destroyed him.

What was he to do next? He was not afraid. As he contemplated his own end he was sad, not for himself, but for his beloved country.

11

"The Roots Will Sprout Again"

THE CANNY OLD LEADER KNEW THAT HIS DREAM HAD collapsed and that his end was probably near. But he did not grow desperate, as the mulatto Rigaud had done before him, and as Christophe and Dessalines were to do after him. Amidst the bloody melodrama, the false heroics and the craven fears of his period, Toussaint stands out for his cool courage.

He lived now on his plantation as he had always lived. His staff was still devoted to him, and he worked with them day and night. Gradually he began drawing more and more of the scattered Haitian army to him. The country around his plantation was filled with soldiers turned farmer. There was a continual coming and going in Toussaint's house of the officers who had not deserted to the French.

Leclerc knew that as long as Toussaint lived in what was virtually an armed camp he could not possibly ar-

168

rest him. Toussaint would have to be lured away. Now Leclerc possessed a kind of low cunning. If he could not catch a man fairly, then he used the man's weakness, or even one of his best qualities, to trap him. Leclerc had learned a lot about Toussaint's character during the war. He knew that the old leader trusted few people. But he also knew that Toussaint had a high sense of honor, and that he would trust absolutely anyone who he thought had a similar sense of honor. Toussaint never broke his word, and it was impossible for him to believe that any man of honor would do so.

There was one officer of the French army whom Toussaint liked and trusted. This was a man named Brunet, who often carried messages from Toussaint to Leclerc. He had always been favorably disposed toward the black leader. Leclerc chose Brunet to carry out his plan. Brunet wrote a friendly letter to Toussaint, in which he spoke of some irritating matters that had come up with Leclerc, and promised that they would be remedied. At the end he added casually that if Toussaint could ride over to spend an hour with him some afternoon they could settle these matters quickly and easily.

The letter was disarming. Toussaint had no reason to suspect it. On the other hand he made a rule of never leaving his plantation. There was too much danger abroad in Haiti these days. For some mysterious reason Toussaint now decided to break his rule and go to see Brunet.

Why did he walk so easily into this trap? He knew that Leclerc wanted to catch him and would stop at nothing. He trusted Brunet, but Brunet might have been fooled. The explanation lies in another side of Toussaint's character—his love of danger and his sense of fatality. All his life Toussaint had taken chances. Like a gambler he trusted his luck. When it was running high, he knew he couldn't lose. He had always escaped miraculously from seemingly deadly situations. Once, when all those around him were shot from ambush, he merely had the plumes of his hat shot off. A messenger was shot while delivering a letter to Toussaint and died in his arms. His coach was fired on just a few minutes after Toussaint had left it to ride ahead on horseback. He had always led his men in the most desperate charges. He had been wounded seventeen times, but never badly.

After ten years of living with constant danger, Toussaint had come to believe in his own luck and his ability to escape from any sort of ambush. This time he was trying fate once more. He was growing tired of the enforced peacefulness of his plantation, and he was ready to court danger again. If something happened to him, so be it. It was Fate.

He rode over to Brunet's house. The French general greeted him with warm friendliness and asked him to wait a few minutes. As Toussaint waited, the door suddenly burst open and a soldier entered with a pistol in one hand and a sword in the other. Behind him were many more soldiers. Toussaint leaped to his feet and

"General Leclerc has ordered your arrest," the soldier told Toussaint

drew his sword, but the soldier's words stopped him.

"General, the Captain General Leclerc has ordered your arrest. Our men are everywhere. If you resist you are a dead man. Your power in Haiti is at an end."

Toussaint kept his sword in his hand and said, "I rely on the protection of General Brunet. He has given me his word of honor."

But Brunet did not appear. The word of honor of this Frenchman was worthless, and Brunet hid himself from Toussaint. Shame was deep in him, and his act of base betrayal was to stay with him the rest of his life. Even his comrades had only contempt for him and spoke of him scornfully as the "policeman."

Toussaint's sword was taken from him by force, and his hands were tied behind his back. Then he was hurried away secretly to the nearest port. No one was to know of the arrest until Toussaint was safely on the high seas.

The moment Toussaint arrived on board, the French frigate of war weighed her anchor and set sail for France. Toussaint looked back at the blue-black mountains and the pale green, fertile valleys of his country. He smelled the strong smells of the city and the heavy, sweet orange blossoms, and above them the mountain

He looked back at the blue-black mountains of Haiti

pines. His own dream was dead, but he knew that his beloved Haiti was not finished.

"In overthrowing me," he said to the ship's captain, "you have cut down in Haiti only the trunk of the tree of liberty. It will spring up again by the roots, for they are numerous and deep."

These were Toussaint's last words on the freedom of his country.

In Haiti Leclerc exulted. "Toussaint is removed!" he wrote to Napoleon. "It is a great victory. I have taken from the blacks their rallying point. He must not be free. Imprison him in the interior of France so that he shall never see Haiti again."

Napoleon didn't need this advice. He had no intention of bringing Toussaint to trial. In the first place he had no accusation against the black leader that would stand up in court. Ever since Toussaint had been in power he had consistently held Haiti for France, and had strengthened and defended it against her enemies.

Even if he could arrange it so that Toussaint were proved guilty and shot as a traitor, Napoleon knew that Toussaint would become a martyr whose spirit would live on. Toussaint had become a symbol of freedom, not only in his own country but all over Europe. Sympathy for the fallen leader was strong. Napoleon knew that the only way he could destroy Toussaint was to hide him away. He would let him rot in a remote fortress until sympathy died down and the old leader was forgotten.

Toussaint was hurried across France to the desolate Jura Mountains, where it is winter eight months of the year and the sun seldom shines. There, on the top of a sheer mountain of solid rock, was a grim fortress surrounded only by snow, ice and forbidding pinnacles. In this dreary place, where the walls were twelve feet thick, the light could hardly penetrate through the slits of windows. The ceilings and walls dripped continuously with moisture. There Toussaint spent the last few months of his life.

Life in the gloomy prison was quickly fatal to him. He brooded, huddled over a tiny fire, suffering horribly from inactivity, cold and bad food. He longed for his native land, the hot sun, the soft blue sky, the gentle wind off the Caribbean, the jungle-covered mountains that he knew so well, the feel of a horse under him

on the tropical plains. Napoleon didn't have to wait long
to get rid of his enemy. On April 7, 1803, ten months
after he had been captured, Toussaint was dead.

As he died the new black leaders in Haiti were drawing up a Declaration of Independence. The roots were
sprouting again. The removal of Toussaint had not put
an end to Haitian defiance as Napoleon and Leclerc had
thought it would. All over the country there were insurrections against the French. Leclerc, sick with yellow
fever, said to his doctor that men who loved liberty as
did the Negroes of Haiti, and men as valiant as the
French soldiers, deserved a better fate than that to
which Napoleon had doomed them. He died full of
remorse and despair, and flaxen-haired Pauline, weeping and desolate, cut off her long tresses and laid them
in his grave. Leclerc's successor, the vain, cruel and
despotic Rochambeau, was increasingly helpless against
the black will to freedom.

Finally Napoleon took stock and reckoned that the indomitable blacks had destroyed a French army of 63,-
000 men. He decided that he had better forget Haiti
and turn the eyes of the world somewhere else before
his reputation as a military genius was entirely lost. He

deliberately provoked England and jumped with both feet into a European war. He turned his back on the dream of a Western empire, and sold the Louisiana Territory to the United States for fifteen million dollars. We were no longer in peril. We owe our safety to the intrepid black slave in Haiti who handed out muskets to his people and whipped Napoleon's proudest army before it could get anywhere near the United States.

Napoleon's adventure in the New World was over, and the failure of the French in Haiti was quickly forgotten. In 1804 the blacks were finally, after all the bloody years, left to their destiny.

What Toussaint had done for his country was not destroyed. He had given to the lowly, oppressed slaves pride and strength and freedom. These things do not die easily. Haiti grew again. There were more years of storm and strife as the black leaders fought for power. But at last, in 1820, Haiti became a United Republic.

To this day the little country stands as a monument to great-hearted Toussaint. There, in one of the few free black republics in the world, Negroes can walk with their heads high, without fear or shame, and they are the equals of anyone on earth.

Index

179

177
- 29
650 PP.

3
24 x 9 = 216 w/p

216
156
1296
1080
216
33696

33700 WORDS

216
150
800
10,800
2 / 24 00 WORDS -
3